Viking Warrior

conditioning

The Scientific Approach to Forging a Heart of Elastic Steel: An application of The Theory Behind Proper VO2max Training

By Kenneth Jay

Viking Warrior Conditioning
By Kenneth Jay

Published in the United States by:
Dragon Door Publications, Inc
P.O. Box 4381, St. Paul, MN 55104
Tel: (651) 487-2180 • Fax: (651) 487-3954
Credit card orders: 1-800-899-5111
Email: support@dragondoor.com • Website: www.dragondoor.com

ISBN: 978-0-938045-04-5   0-938045-04-0

This edition first published in March 2009

Printed in the United States of America

Book design, Illustrations, logos, photo manipulation and cover by Derek Brigham
Website http//www.dbrigham.com• Tel/Fax: (763) 208-3069 • Email: dbrigham@visi.com
Photographs of Kenneth Jay by Hanne Paludan Kristensen • www.hpkristensen.dk,
Photographs on pages 96-98 by RalphDeHaan.com

DISCLAIMER
The author and publisher of this material are not responsible in any manner whatsoever for any injury that may occur through following the instructions contained in this material. The activities, physical and otherwise, described herein for informational purposes only, may be too strenuous or dangerous for some people and the reader(s) should consult a physician before engaging in them.

— TABLE OF CONTENTS —

FOREWORD

BY MARK REIFKIND
MASTER INSTRUCTOR RKC

It's not often in the world of physical training that something comes along so special, so unique, and so effective that it causes a paradigm shift in how people train and think about training. Louie Simmons turned the powerlifting world upside down with his inspired reinvention of how to train the powerlift. Pavel did the same thing and more with the Russian Kettlebell Challenge. And now, Kenneth Jay has taken the Tsar of the Kettlebell lifts—the kettlebell snatch—and created a method of training so revolutionary that it causes us to rethink *everything* we thought we knew about cardiovascular training and how to incorporate it into our strength and conditioning programs.

Kenneth has looked at the true meaning of cardiovascular adaptation and configured a kettlebell-training program to elicit that response for real. As I told him when we were discussing the benefits I had derived from this, "The VO2max training delivers what circuit training only promised: real strength and cardiovascular conditioning in the same package. With NO compromises."

I remember sitting in the auditorium at the Level 2 RKC Certification when Kenneth unveiled this new regime and I heard him speak about building a heart of "elastic steel" using only the 16 kg kettlebell. I was able to snatch the 24 kg bell quite well at the time but was still suffering from shoulder issues that precluded me from really going all out with it. My powerlifter's mindset would not allow me to use lighter bells, as that would be "too sissy," to quote a top-level Russian Kettlebell Chief Instructor. But as a volume-training addict, the program intrigued me.

I was even more intrigued when I got to witness the RKC candidates being put through their paces in this new way of using the kettlebell. It looked brutal but quite safe—a great combination for this high-mileage, ex-competitive athlete. I had to try it as soon as I got back home. And what an eye-opener it was!

Having gotten permission to use a lighter bell, I felt quite safe focusing on moving the weight as quickly as I could during the snatches and trying to do the prescribed number of sets and reps. *Trying* is the operative word. I stopped counting when my heart rate topped 190 and I wasn't even halfway through the workout.

As an ex-gymnast, I have always reveled in the speed and momentum training that kettlebell work not only allows but encourages. I immediately realized that the magic in the bell was able to really develop speed and, with speed, power. And as we all know, in the world of sport, speed and power are the king and queen. This new VO2max training program maximized both these attributes to the hilt, all the while using weights that were so safe that anyone could do them—anyone who could handle the workload, that is!

Always being one to take a long-term approach and giving my injuries their due, I adapted the program to just one day a week, not really thinking I would be able to garner all the benefits from such a modification. But in just eight weeks of doing the workout religiously once a week, in addition to my other KB training, my resting heart rate dropped from 64 to 48! It hadn't been that low since I had trained for ultramarathons and triathlons! Kenneth was really, really on to something special.

I also put my clients who were snatching on the system, and they saw results so quickly that it was mind blowing: improved cardiovascular efficiency, loss of fat, and increased speed and power. Also, their snatch training went to a new level in so short a time that it was almost not to be believed.

It may seem impossible, but just two or three sessions of this program produced changes in people's bodies and systems. Hard to believe, but it was happening right in front of my eyes—and all with kettlebells light enough not to scare away the most timid of clients. When something works, it works! Kenneth truly understands the meaning of force: mass x acceleration. Acceleration is clearly the lynchpin here.

My wife, Tracy, who at the time was in phenomenal shape from high-volume kettlebell training, also took to the program in a heartbeat and saw even more body fat loss and muscular definition than she had thought possible—and from just one session per week. Kenneth had really figured out something very unique.

The training program really forces you to hit on all cylinders at once: speed, power, efficiency of movement (you can't go fast if you're inefficient), mental and physical toughness, and, of course, the cardiovascular system of a miler with the muscular power of a gymnast. What a great combination!

One year later, at the next Level 2 RKC Certification, Kenneth unveiled his latest addition to the VO2max program—the BOOST, a peaking protocol—and again, he put the candidates through their paces after the lecture. This was another eye-opener, especially to Tracy, who had been training with the regular program religiously. She knew this would be the ticket to putting her Secret Service Snatch Test (SSST) numbers over the top.

Now with this amazing book, Kenneth has put it all down on paper. All the science, all the protocols, and all the progressions. He has added even more protocols to the original program, and all have real research to back them up. This is not an easy read, just as the protocols are not easy to do. Simple but not easy, as I love to say.

After a year more of doing VO2max workouts every week, everything has changed about my snatch training. All for the good! I can now snatch twice a week with no shoulder issues, and I could do three sessions, if I wanted. The speed and power I got from using the 16 kg bell has transferred to my 24 kg snatch work, and I can now snatch the 24 kg as quickly and powerfully as the 16 kg. My conditioning is at an all-time high, as is my recovery ability. My resting heart rate is still low, as is my body fat level, but my muscle mass is as high as it's been in years. And now with this book and these new protocols, there will be no lack of progression or growth in my snatch training or my conditioning in the coming months. I can continue unabated along the path of mastery of the kettlebell snatch for power and conditioning.

Kenneth has taken the concepts of deep skill and internal focus—the hallmarks of the RKC system—and created a method that is revolutionary yet accessible to virtually anyone who can snatch a kettlebell. Of course, he or she must also have the intestinal fortitude and desire to have the heart of a racehorse and the strength of a grizzly—worthy goals, to say the least.

If art is where science and intuition meet, then Instructor Kenneth Jay has truly created a work of art. Thank you, my brother! This training will serve me well for many, many years, as it will the multitudes who take up the challenge. Thank you for developing ilt. I know it will stand the test of time.

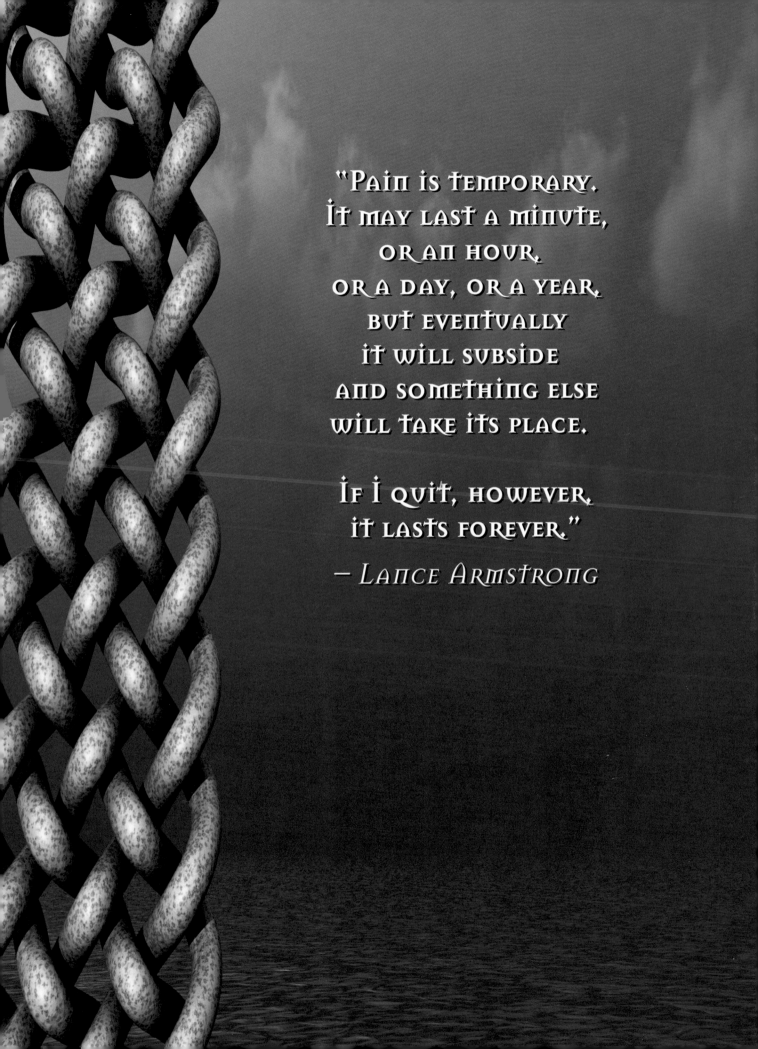

"Pain is temporary.
It may last a minute,
or an hour,
or a day, or a year,
but eventually
it will subside
and something else
will take its place.

If I quit, however,
it lasts forever."
— Lance Armstrong

Introduction

Back in ancient Greece, in the days of the battle at the Hot Gates, human beings had superior genetics compared to people in this lifetime. A couple of years ago, an experiment was conducted across history. Exercise physiologists, engineers, and historians from several universities across Europe set out to determine the level of conditioning that these heroes of ancient times possessed. An historical analysis of information on these men's training, ability to sail ships, and ability to cover great distances by foot while wearing armor showed that the cardiovascular endurance and strength of the average man would be hard, if not impossible, to match today, even among world-level athletes. It would be hard today to find enough world-class athletes in the entire world to row a *single replica* of an ancient battleship at the same speed and for the same duration as men from the past were able to do. Today, we would not stand a chance against these men. Our genetics have changed, and we are in the worst shape ever!

It is not a coincidence that the men of the past were in such excellent cardiovascular health. Training and fighting a lot requires being able to exert sustained force and generate great acceleration *while* being under tremendous cardiovascular stress. This is the secret of ancient Viking warrior conditioning.

The key to the performance level of the glory days is right in front of us. The kettlebell will deliver a heart of elastic steel with superior flexibility and contractile force generation.

I urge you to reclaim the past! Take a stand and gain the heart of a racehorse with the strength of a grizzly. That would make the heroes of the past proud.

As the immortal slogan from the Russian military puts it:

"If you don't know how, I'll teach you.
If you don't want to, I'll make you!"

I
VIKING WARRIOR
Conditioning

"So you think a fight is one blow? One kick? Until you can put combinations together without thinking, until you learn how to keep moving, and to endure, hire a bodyguard or lead a less aggressive life."—*Bruce Lee*

Bruce Lee said these words back in 1971, and as he did in so many other aspects of life, he hit the nail on the head. Being able to move with high intensity for prolonged periods of time is, in many ways, crucial for success if you are a fighter, in the military, working in law enforcement, or doing any other activity that requires multiple bursts of movement. With no endurance, you will not be successful in these kinds of activities, no matter how big you bench.

Bruce used to say that technique and strength are useless if you lack the requisite endurance to carry them out. He ran every day to maintain his fighting edge. The man was clearly ahead of his time.

Cardiovascular training is definitely necessary if you want to be able to maintain a high level of performance over several minutes. Do not mistake this type of cardio training for doing sissified, low-intensity, pink dumbbell Jane Fonda–robics, as a certain Russian might put it. Instead, think of it as intermittent, high-powered work at maximal or supramaximal intensity in the correct ratio of work and rest. Even popular intervals protocols like the Tabata do not quite cut it, because the work/rest/volume ratios are not optimized for developing a heart of elastic steel. But utilizing what we now know about exercise physiology, we can extract maximum benefit from interval training.

Bruce dug running, and it is still a great form of exercise. I like the kettlebell. No, scratch that: I LOVE the kettlebell, and I find it to be an exceptional tool for this kind of training.

If the example of Bruce Lee does not convince you of the need for cardiovascular training (true cardio, that is), then allow me to elaborate on the subject. Basically, what it comes down to is that the less time you have for recovery, the more important your maximal oxygen uptake becomes.

For example, consider two professional boxers. They have to endure 12 three-minute rounds of high-powered explosive movements, each new round coming after only one minute of rest. If these two fighters have equal skill, equal strength, equal speed, and so on but differ in oxygen uptake, the one with the higher uptake will be victorious. He will be able to recover more during the rest periods and the actual rounds when the fighters are at a distance from one another and can relax their muscles. The fighter with the higher oxygen uptake will be able to put out *more power* as the fight progresses, because he will be better at buffering the build-up of metabolites in the muscles. In the context of combat, better conditioning translates into greater power!

It is definitely true that you need to train anaerobically, but if you are really serious, you should also train your ability to recover from intense bouts. As Bruce Lee's son, Brandon, explains, "If you try and do a three-minute round with me, I don't care how big and strong your muscles are, if you don't have a real good cardiovascular system, you're going to be dead in about forty-five seconds and you better watch out—because I'm still gonna be punching!"

This is exactly what drove me to investigate training with the kettlebell for its ability to produce maximal oxygen uptake values. It has been shown without a shred of doubt that if you want to increase your maximal oxygen uptake, you should train at or slightly above an intensity level that elicits your maximal oxygen uptake value. Forget about slow, low-intensity, long-distance stuff and turn it up!

The next requirement is to choose an exercise that has the potential to do this. My exercise of choice is the kettlebell snatch. No other kettlebell exercise or combination of kettlebell exercises has the potential to produce the desired level of oxygen uptake like the snatch.

Lastly, choose the right exercise protocol. Believe me, it *does* matter how you set up your work-to-rest (work:rest) ratio and the snatch cadence. The work:rest ratio, together with the chosen cadence, will determine the training response you get. There are several good structured protocols and about a million bad ones. Guessing leads to inferior results. I, for one, am not content with that, and neither should you. Even if you are not an elite athlete, you should still use the best protocols for your physical development. Proper planning and structuring of training sessions will ensure maximum results and prevent poor performance. Don't settle for anything less than optimal. Learn proven protocols and why they work.

My mission is to dispel the myths of cardio training so you can benefit from those science-based and trench-tested protocols that will turn your body into a lean, power-packed Viking Warrior—worthy of Thor, the God of Thunder, himself.

Before we get into the exact protocols, let's take a look at the science behind them.

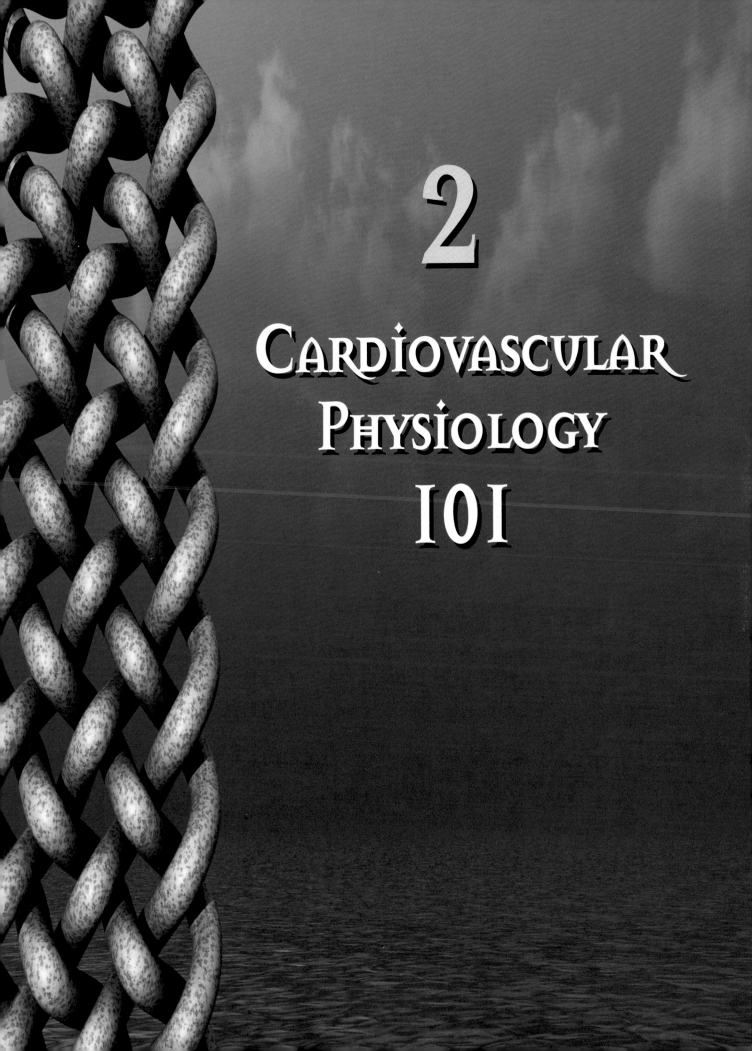

2

CARDIOVASCULAR PHYSIOLOGY 101

I cannot help the complexity of the human body. I wish its physiology could be simpler and easier to comprehend, but unfortunately, that is not the case. Let me give you an idea of how complex it really is.

The human body and the way it functions has been studied for centuries, and in this modern era, we are, with the help of technology, uncovering the mysteries of the human body faster than ever before. However, that does not mean that we are even close to figuring out how this magnificent system of interrelated, co-dependent, energetic chemical structures functions. If we imagine the human body as the size of a football field, then we have to date uncovered what amounts to a postage stamp—a small one. So, if the scientists are limited in their understanding of the human body, I can do only my best to present what is known about physiology in an accessible fashion.

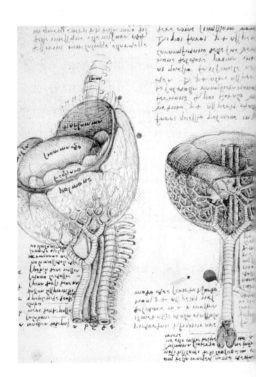

If you are not interested in the physiology behind training the VO2max, feel free to skip this chapter. I promise that it will not diminish the results you will get from the Viking Warrior Conditioning regime. Just remember, as Pavel says, "The Party is always right!"

However, should you find yourself in need of explaining what this kind of training does, then steal the elevator pitch, which follows.

THE ELEVATOR PITCH

At the 2008 Level II RKC Certification, I was asked if I could provide an elevator pitch for the training power of the Viking Warrior Conditioning regime. I had given it quite a lot of thought, but Master RKC Mark Reifkind was the one who came up with the following: "The Viking Warrior Conditioning regime delivers what the original circuit-training idea promised: a cardiovascular training effect in conjunction with strength endurance development." Basically, this kind of training will strengthen your heart, as well as your muscles, while boosting your metabolism and ridding you of any unwanted fat deposits—guaranteed and scientifically proven!

Still with me?
Good, here we go

In 2006, the very first Western-based university study on the kettlebell was conducted. Oxygen uptake (VO2), lactate production, energy output, and power were all measured and analyzed in terms of doing conventional types of cardiovascular training. The kettlebell snatch delivered results every bit as good as conventional types of exercise, when done correctly.

In addition, the kettlebell snatch displayed a major advantage: It is ballistic and employs the Valsalva pressurization technique during each repetition. So, not only do you stimulate an expansion of the heart wall (called *eccentric hypertrophy*), and thereby an increase in maximal oxygen uptake (VO2max), but you also stimulate an increase in the thickness of the heart wall (called *concentric hypertrophy*). These effects, along with increases in blood pressure sensitivity and arterial compliance, aren't observed to the same extent with other types of cardiovascular activities.

Let's dig a little more into the science. The VO2 is defined as the amount of oxygen uptake on a whole-body level in a given time period. When we are talking about the VO2max, we are talking about the maximal oxygen uptake on a whole-body level in a given time period.

Everything can be expressed mathematically, since mathematics is the universal language:

VO2 = Cardiac Output (CO) x Arterial-Venous Oxygen Difference (A-V O2-diff)

The oxygen uptake equals the cardiac output multiplied by the difference in blood oxygen of the arterial and venous circulatory system. Hence, the maximal VO2, or the VO2max, is the maximal cardiac output multiplied by the maximal A-V O2-diff, or expressed mathematically:

VO2max = COmax x A-V O2-diffmax

This leads to the definition of the cardiac output and the A-V O2-diff. The cardiac output, or CO, is defined as the heart rate (HR, measured in beats per minute, or bpm) multiplied by the stroke volume (SV):

CO = Heart Rate (HR) x Stroke Volume (SV)

To elaborate, the A-V O2 differentiate has been defined as the oxygen content of the blood going to the working muscles minus the oxygen content of the blood going from the working muscles and returning to the heart. Another way of saying that is that the A-V O2-diff is the working muscle maximal oxygen extraction capacity.

Finally, the stroke volume (SV) has to be defined. It is the volume of blood in the filling phase of the heart (left-ventricular end, diastolic volume) minus the ejection of blood in each heartbeat (left-ventricular end, systolic volume). The stroke volume is basically the amount of blood ejected from the heart with every beat, or expressed mathematically:

SV = EDV – ESV (for the left ventricle of the heart)

To understand completely what it requires to stimulate an adaptation to an increased VO2max, we have to look at each part of the VO2 equation and then at VO2 kinetics, which I will come back to.

The VO2 equation tells us that to increase VO2max, we can increase either CO or A-V O2-difference or both. CO can be increased by an increase in HR or SV or both. Since it is not really possible to increase HR beyond a certain point and the maximal, HR doesn't really change significantly after training (it may even drop, due to reduced left ventricular filling time during maximal exertion), the SV is the factor to concentrate on when wanting to increase maximal CO.

Remember that the SV is the maximal filling of the heart (EDV) minus the maximal ejection of blood (ESV). So, a change in either will result in a change in SV. Two important factors in increasing the SV are preload and afterload. *Preload* is determined mainly by how much blood returns to the heart. The more blood that returns, the more the heart fills up with blood, thus increasing the EDV. This is called the *Frank-Starling mechanism. Afterload* is the load or force against which the heart has to contract to eject blood. This factor is determined mainly by the aortic pressure, which is the pressure the heart has to overcome when ejecting blood. The greater the aortic pressure, the greater the afterload on the heart, which thus increases the ESV and thereby reduces the SV, because SV equals EDV minus ESV.

A number of other factors are also involved in regulating the SV. For instance, the compliance of the heart is very important. If the compliance is high, the preload is high, and vice versa. The *compliance* of the heart is reduced with the increased hypertrophy of the heart wall, which is a direct result of increased afterload. Since the afterload is determined by the pressure the heart has to overcome to eject blood and that pressure increases during weightlifting, the main factor responsible for increased hypertrophy (and thereby reduced compliance of the heart) is lifting weights.

So, why does the aortic pressure rise during weight training? When a person lifts a weight and braces the midsection of the body, the intrapleural pressure rises, which causes an increase in aortic pressure and thereby an increase in afterload. In addition, the large increase in intrapleural pressure causes a decrease in the amount of blood returning to the heart, which is caused by an increase in venous resistance, and thereby reduces the SV by reducing the filling of the heart.

The other part of the VO2 equation is the extraction of oxygen in the working muscles. When you begin exercise, your CO is increased by sympathetic nervous system activation and muscle pump activation. The nervous system increases HR in an anticipatory fashion, and the muscle pump increases the venous return of blood to the heart, which increases preload and thereby SV by the Frank-Starling mechanism, as previously mentioned. Local muscular metabolic mechanisms cause dilation of blood vessels to increase bloodflow.

However, if the activity of the agonist and antagonist muscles is not coordinated in a fast, rhythmical pattern, then blood perfusion of the muscles will be limited, because the muscles will be contracting and squeezing the vessels, so no oxygen exchange will take place. This scenario occurs when lifting weights. The A-V O2 difference will be very low, because the time between blood perfusion/vessel constriction/blood reperfusion will be relatively long. The lack of oxygen will cause an increase in HR, increased sympathetic activation, and decreased parasympathetic activation but no increase in CO because of the increase in venous resistance—the muscles squeezing the vessels.

To sum up, increasing EDV, decreasing ESV, or both stimulate an increase in VO2max. HR has little to do with it, because the maximal HR cannot be increased; hence, it cannot increase CO. The nature of the activity can determine the VO2max by limiting the muscle blood perfusion so little or no oxygen extraction occurs. This will cause an increase in HR, due to the lack of oxygen and reduced venous blood return. This will not increase CO because of the reduced preload (venous blood return).

It should be evident by now that HR is not always an entirely valid indication of good cardio stimulation. HR is valid as an indication of the VO2 when talking about activities like running, cycling, skiing, and swimming—all of which provide relatively little resistance on the muscles and thereby create very little time between blood perfusion/constriction/blood reperfusion.

A lot of studies have been conducted on this phenomenon. The relationship of VO2 as a function of HR is linearly related, with a factor of approximately 1.2. Table 1 shows this connection.

Table 1: Relationship Between VO2 and HR Function

% HRmax	% VO2max
50 (low-intensity exercise)	28
60 (low-intensity)	40
70 (low- to medium- intensity)	58
80 (medium-intensity)	70
90 (high-intensity)	83
100 (high-intensity)	100

For example, take a person with a maximal HR of 200 bpm. He or she goes for a run at 90% HR. If he or she would run at around 83% of VO2max, then HR would be 180 bpm. This intensity would be considered high. To make any cardiovascular adaptation, the American College of Sports Medicine (ACSM) recommends that cardio training be at least 55% VO2max or around 70% HRmax for a sedentary person.

Then what about kettlebell training? What is the correlation between HR and VO2, you might be wondering? Well, first of all, kettlebell training is not just one exercise, so it is impossible to say anything in general about kettlebell training. However, considering the ACSM requirements for making VO2 adaptations, the kettlebell snatch does the trick.

The reason for this is that a lot of muscle mass is involved, and the snatch is the exercise where the kettlebell travels the longest distance in the shortest amount of time, making it the most dynamic. The swing comes close, but the bell travels a shorter distance. Also, in the swing, there is less oxygen extraction in the muscles of the upper body because of the static work. In the snatch, the bending of the elbow, the "punch through," and the brief stop or turn at the lockout make all the difference.

The high-intensity repetition of the kettlebell snatch provides a stimulus that is a combination of adaptation to an increased VO2max by an increased SV (EDV) and hypertrophy of the walls of the heart, as seen with weight training. However, there is reason to believe that even though the walls of the heart thicken, the compliance increases, which is the very opposite of what is normally seen during weight training. Also, it is very easy to speculate that the baroreceptor sensitivity is increased during kettlebell snatches. This is beneficial, since the baroreceptors are responsible for registering blood pressure changes.

The increase in heart wall thickness, along with increased compliance, increased baroreceptor sensitivity, and expansion of the heart chambers, makes the kettlebell snatch special. These factors separate snatching from activities like running and cycling, which do not deliver an increase in wall thickness. The reason for this is probably found in the use of the Valsalva maneuver during repetition snatches, which is necessary to stabilize the body under load. The thickness of the heart wall is an expression of how strong the heart can contract (inotrophy of the heart). Basically, it means that a thicker muscle is stronger than a thin muscle—and having a stronger heart musculature is a good thing!

So, what happens exactly when you start exercising with the kettlebell? I'm glad you asked! Let's look at the physiological adaptations to cardiovascular exercise with the kettlebell.

CENTRAL EFFECTS

The research literature tells us that there are significant differences between a trained and untrained body in terms of the effects of performing a prolonged, dynamic, full-body workout. In a well-trained body, the stroke volume during rest increases, due mainly to increased heart inotrophy and eccentric hypertrophy. This leads to a drop in resting heart rate, because during rest, the cardiac output is constant. Remember the formula?

CO = HR x SV

No change in maximal heart rate is observed, which means there will be a bigger difference between the resting heart rate and maximal heart rate in a well-trained individual. A well-trained individual will have a larger maximal stroke volume at increasing and maximal intensities because of an increased end diastolic volume (EDV) in the left ventricle of the heart. There are three reasons for this: (1) eccentric hypertrophy of the heart, (2) increased compliance of the heart, and (3) increased end diastolic filling pressure. These factors help to explain about 50% of the increase in the VO2max of a well-trained individual. When the stroke volume increases, the cardiac output also increases, and when the oxygen extraction of the working muscles (the A-V O2 difference) increases, the VO2max goes up in a trained individual.

In addition, a well-trained individual has an increased *ejection fraction* of up to 90%, compared to a 75% rating for an untrained individual. The ejection fraction is the relationship between the stroke volume and end diastolic volume, meaning that more blood will be ejected from the left ventricle of the heart with every heartbeat. The heart does not empty the ventricle completely with every heartbeat, because of pressure-gated channels within it. However, in a well-trained individual, the heart will empty about 90%, which is noticeably more than the 75% that's characteristic of an untrained individual.

Adaptations include (but are not limited to) the following:

CIRCULATORY SYSTEM: HEART

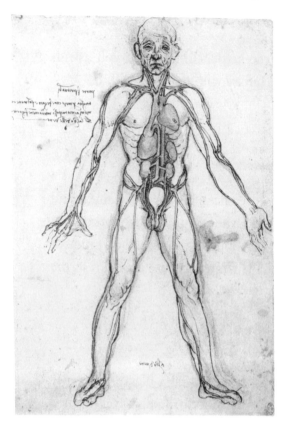

- ⊙ Increased heart volume and weight
- ⊙ Increased baroreceptor sensitivity
- ⊙ Increased compliance
- ⊙ Increased capillary density of the heart
- ⊙ Eccentric hypertrophy of the heart
- ⊙ Concentric hypertrophy of the heart (in this context good, but otherwise bad)
- ⊙ Increased left ventricular–End diastolic volume (LV–EDV)
- ⊙ Increased power in the contractile muscle fibers of the heart
- ⊙ Increased stroke volume during rest and submaximal and maximal exercise
- ⊙ Decreased heart rate during rest and submaximal and maximal exercise
- ⊙ Increased volume of bloodflow per minute during maximal exercise
- ⊙ Increased ejection fraction
- ⊙ Decreased blood pressure
- ⊙ Decreased oxygen consumption at submaximal exercise level
- ⊙ Increased oxygen consumption at maximal exercise level

RESPIRATION

- ⊙ Increased endurance and strength of respiratory muscles
- ⊙ Decreased ventilation at submaximal exercise intensity
- ⊙ Increased ventilation at maximal exercise intensity
- ⊙ Increased rate of oxygen transport from the lungs to the bloodstream

PERIPHERAL EFFECTS

Peripheral adaptations of cardiovascular exercise will start very quickly, including increases in mitochondrial density, oxidative enzyme capacity, and capillary density. These factors will influence the body's ability to burn fat and carbohydrates. Oxidative enzymes such as citrate synthase (CS), succinate dehydrogenase (SDH), and beta hydroxy CoA dehydrogenase (HAD) will increase very rapidly. Having larger quantities of enzymes means that more fat and carbohydrates can be burned in the muscles.

CS and SDH are limiting factors in the Krebs cycle, and HAD is a limiting factor in beta-oxidation, which is basically the conversion of fat to something called Acetyl CoA, a substance that fuels the Krebs cycle. If the amounts of all of these enzymes increase, then the aerobic energy turnover will increase. When that happens, a given amount of work will be fueled by fat in a trained individual to a larger extent than in an untrained individual. In addition to burning more fat, the trained individual will spare valuable muscle and liver glycogen.

When the capillary density in muscle tissue increases, the oxygen mean transit time (MTT) also increases. This results in an increase in the timeframe for gas and substrate exchange in the working muscles. In combination with the central effects of cardiovascular training, the peripheral effects will increase the work capacity of the trained individual.

Adaptations include (but are not limited to) the following:

⊙ Increased numbers of glucose transporters

⊙ Increased capillary density of muscles

⊙ Increased activity of aerobic ATP formation enzymatic activity (such as citrate synthrase and succinate dehydrogenase, which are important in Krebs cycle)

⊙ Increased bloodflow to the muscles

⊙ Increased free fatty acid uptake from the blood

⊙ Decreased rate of lactic acid production at a given intensity level

⊙ Increased insulin sensitivity

These are just some of the benefits you will receive by incorporating the cardiovascular kettlebell training regime in your exercise program. Basically, if you want to be able to perform longer at a given intensity level and to be able to recover faster from anaerobic spurts, this is the way to go.

UNDERSTANDING VO2 KINETICS

When exercise commences, the immediate response of the circulatory system is to increase cardiac output. It will take some time, however, before the cardiovascular system catches up with the demands of exercise. This basically means that your anaerobic energy system will provide the energy needed until your cardiac output catches up. This is also called the kinetics of the oxygen uptake.

Figure 1: Graphic Description of VO2 Kinetics

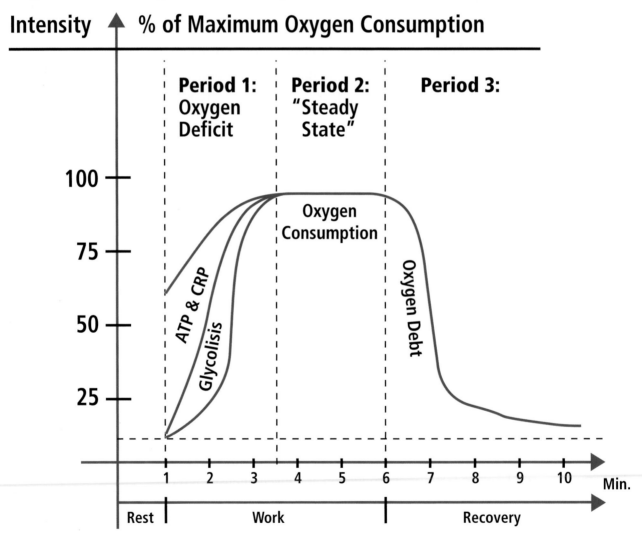

When exercise commences, the energy demand during the first three to four minutes will be covered by ATP, PCr, glycolysis, and, to an increasing extent, the anaerobic energy system. This is Period 1 of the VO2 kinetics and is referred to as the *oxygen deficit period*. During Period 2, the VO2 is in a *steady state*, which means the energy requirement is matched by an equally large oxygen uptake. (In this context, the term steady state does not refer to continuous exercise.) When the exercise is terminated, an oxygen debt has to be repaid (Period 3).

Figure 1 is a graphic description of how the oxygen uptake/consumption increases when you begin an exercise activity. Every time you start exercising, you have an oxygen deficit for about three or four minutes. This means that your oxygen uptake is *not* adequate to meet your body's oxygen demands. During this first period, the energy needed will be provided by anaerobic sources, such as stored ATP (adenosine triphosphate, the fuel your body converts all energy sources into), PCr (creatine phosphate, the "jet fuel" of the body, of which we have enough to go all out for 10 seconds), and glycolysis (which is the conversion of carbohydrates into ATP with lactic acid as a by-product). The primary reason for this phenomenon is that the circulatory system has a somewhat slow response time, which is related linearly to the exercise intensity.

After the initial three or four minutes of exercise, a steady state of oxygen uptake/consumption is reached, which means your body has the exact amount of oxygen it needs to sustain the intensity level of the workout. At this point, there is little or no lactate formation (see Figure 1, Period 2). When you finish your workout, you will pay a price, which is called the *oxygen debt* (Period 3). In effect, you have to pay back the amount of oxygen that you needed but did not get during Period 1.

WHY DOES IT MATTER?

Understanding VO2 kinetics is important because it provides information on how the body's energy systems interact to meet its energy demands. Understanding VO2 kinetics also gives you a basis for structuring workouts with the correct work:rest ratio. This is especially important when dealing with intervals. If the rest break becomes too long, the oxygen uptake will drop significantly (Period 3). If the work set is not calibrated at the correct intensity with the correct duration for the correct volume, the oxygen uptake may not have sufficient time to increase before the next rest break.

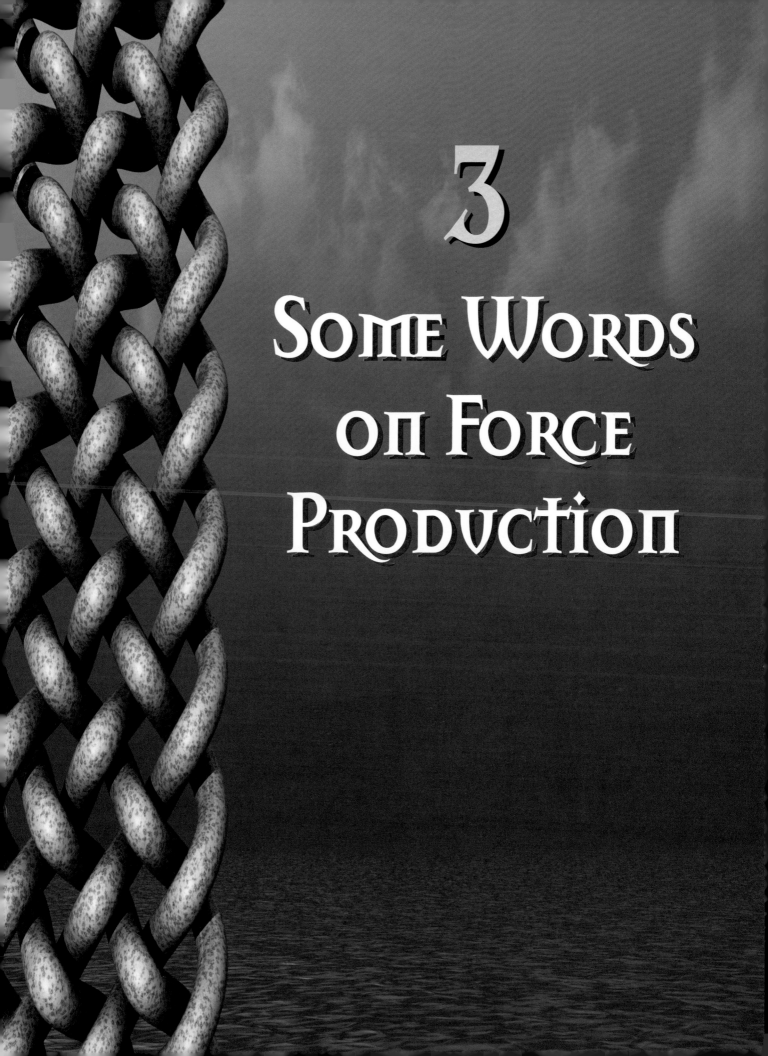

3
SOME WORDS
ON FORCE
PRODUCTION

"In sport, speed is king" write the authors of *Sports Speed*, a great book on developing speed in track-and-field athletes. I will continue the sentence by adding "and to get speed, you need to be able to generate a high force in an extremely short amount of time." Also referred to as the *rate of force development*, this is probably the most important feature of the mind/muscle coordination system.

Defining force

According to Newton's second law of motion, force equals mass multiplied by acceleration. In scientific terms:

Force = Mass x Acceleration

Force can be increased in three ways: (1) by increasing the mass of the object, (2) by increasing the acceleration of the object, and (3) by increasing both mass and acceleration at the same time.

Defining the rate of force development

The maximum rate of rise in muscle force (rate of force development) determines the force that can be generated in the early phase of muscle contraction (0 to 200 milliseconds). In Figure 2, look at the two moment-to-time curves, which are labeled Pretraining and Posttraining. The rate of force development can be defined as the inclination of the slope from the times of 0 to 200 milliseconds. The slope is steeper in the Posttraining curve, meaning that a higher force (moment) is developed in the same timeframe compared to the Pretraining value. Note that the maximum force is not obtained in this timeframe, as the moment values continue to rise slowly until reaching a peak at around 600 milliseconds.

If you are involved in any sport that requires you to accelerate, decelerate, move quickly, change direction, sprint, jump, or the like, then your ability to generate high forces quickly will determine your success.

Figure 2: Moment-to-Time Curves: Pretraining versus Posttraining

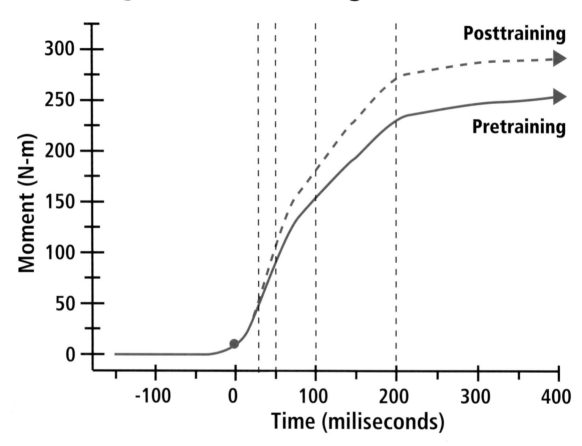

Then what is power?

If strength is your ability to overcome inertia by generating force, and RFD is your explosive ability, then what is power? *Power* can be defined in several ways:

Power = Force x Velocity

or

Power = Force x Distance/Time

If we keep the distance constant, we end up with this formula:

Power = Force/Time

MUSCLE ACTIONS

Muscle tissue is unique in that it can develop force in response to an electrical stimulation carried by the nerves from the motor cortex, which is the area of the brain involved with controlling movement. When a muscle responds, the force it develops is applied to the bones, resulting in a turning effect or torque about the joint between the bones. The movement or lack thereof depends on the level of stimulation and thereby the degree of force it produces. There are three possible outcomes:

1. *Isometric (static) action:* The torque generated by the muscle is equal to the resistance torque. No movement will occur.

2. *Concentric action:* The torque generated by the muscle is greater than the resistance torque. The muscle will shorten, and the bones will move.

3. *Eccentric action:* A greater torque opposes the torque generated by the muscle. The muscle will lengthen, and the bones will move.

During most movement, an eccentric action precedes the concentric action. This is usually referred to as a *stretch-shortening cycle* (SSC). Now, why is this prestretch loading of the muscles and connective tissue so important? The loading is necessary to pre-tense the muscle with sufficient force that can be volitionally generated, so it can be used to execute a movement to go higher, further, or faster.

A simple test will help you understand this idea. Drop into a quarter-squat position, and stay there for five to ten seconds; then jump as high as you can. (This is referred to as a *squat jump.*) Note the height, and then get ready for another jump. This time, do a counter-movement jump, in which you quickly drop into the quarter-squat and then immediately reverse the movement into a jump. Note the height this time, and then compare the two jumps. Which was higher? The second jump, right? Prestretching the muscles enabled you to achieve greater acceleration, thereby creating a greater force with which to execute the movement.

Training for Explosiveness and Power

So, why not just increase the mass of the object? According to Newton's second law of motion, this should also result in an increase in force production. Newton was exactly right, and you will experience an increase in the rate of force development when you train heavy—but only up to a certain point. The nervous system is a complex, coherent network, and it changes in accordance with the stimuli it is subjected to. This plasticity will eventually cause stagnation in the rate of force development and power if only heavy weights are used. The nervous system simply adapts to the slow, grinding execution of heavy lifting, which is why you have to use both approaches in your quest for explosive strength and power.

The time it takes to develop a high force is of utmost importance, especially considering that generating maximum force takes around 600 milliseconds to develop. Look at activities like sprinting and jumping, in which the foot has a surface contact of only 100 to 200 milliseconds—simply not enough time to generate full force potential. On this subject, Häkkinen and Kraemer write, "Training slowly enhances slow speed development but has little carry-over to faster velocities and conversely high speed training has little carry-over to slower speed force development. This is a basic concept as a function of training."

This concept was figured out several decades ago in the Soviet Union. Dr. Michael Yessis, a co-worker of Professor Yuri Verkoshansky and Dr. Mel Siff and editor of the *Soviet Sports Review*, writes the following:

> *Soviet studies show that while strength is an important foundation for avoiding injuries, it is beneficial only up to a certain point for enhancing explosiveness. If you are doing strength training for the first time, your enhanced strength will undoubtedly make you a better athlete. But over the years, if you concentrate only on strength, this can eventually become a detriment, not an aid, to performance.*

Yessis continues:

> *What is the alternative? Rather than seeking to build only muscle, why not go for some explosiveness as well? In general, strength is developed by using high resistance and low repetitions. By contrast, though, speed and explosiveness require a different tactic—relatively low resistance and rapid execution.*

An interesting example to consider

A typical high-level, male shot putter has no problem benching 240 to 250 kg (528 to 550 lbs.), which is 120 to 125 kg (264 to 275 lbs.) of push force per arm. When the shot putter actually thrusts the shot, however, only about 60 kg (132 lbs.) of force is measured, or 50% of his potential.

Which approach should the shot putter take in his training? He could increase his benchpress to, say, 286 kg (629.2 lbs.), a 20% increase, and be able to put 71.5 kg (157.3 lbs.) of force into the shot, or he could work on his rate of force development and power and be able to apply a bigger percentage of his 240 kg (528 lbs.) benchpress. Increasing his potential 20% would bring him to a whopping 84 kg (185 lbs.) of force production in the shot put.

This is no joke! Consider what would take the longest and the most amount of work yet yield the best result. To me, the answer to this question is obvious.

4

Why the Kettlebell?

The fact that you are reading this tells me that you already have an idea why the kettlebell is great for developing general explosive power and supercharging your cardiovascular system. But allow me to explain it anyway!

Acceleration increases when doing ballistic kettlebell exercises with an emphasis on overspeed eccentric action in the negative portion of the swing or snatch. The term *overspeed eccentrics* refers simply to pulling the kettlebell down faster that gravity does on its own. The mechanics to achieve this come from quickly contracting your latissimus dorsi (the lat) and explosively pushing back your hips. Think of the hip motion as punching with your butt. Doing this will result in outrunning gravity, thereby increasing the force generated with a rapid prestretch of the hip extensor muscles. Doing so will also ensure proper spinal stabilization, which is necessary to avoid doing a faceplant. If the midsection stabilizers are not firing, then outrunning gravity will not be possible without falling over.

When the movement is reversed—going from an eccentric loading on your hip extensors to a concentric contraction—it can be termed a SSC. And because the velocity changes so rapidly during the SSC, a high force will be generated quickly, making the movement explosive. This rapid force generation stimulates the ability of the working muscles to develop the rate of force. This translates into a steeper slope on the force-to-time curve during the first couple of tenths of the second after you initiate the repetition. The power of a single repetition also increases, because the time spent doing the repetition drops, meaning that the kettlebell will travel at a greater average velocity. Remember the first equation of power?

Power = Force x Velocity

Furthermore, if you snatch the kettlebell at a rapid pace, like you are supposed to during the Viking Warrior Conditioning regime, the *average* power output during each set of repetition snatches will also increase, because you will not be spending time in the locked-out position.

More power means more energy spent, which requires a greater caloric requirement. The rapid pace is also the key to stimulating your cardiovascular system and increasing your VO2max. The most beautiful part of it all is that none of these benefits exists without the really fast accelerations coming from the overspeed eccentrics and the explosive concentric contractions.

So, many benefits are provided by one simple tool.
How can anyone not want to snatch a kettlebell?

Now, go get a heart of elastic steel with the strength of
a rhino and the endurance of a racehorse!

5

APPLICATION

T he next question is, how can this knowledge be applied? Well, I'm glad you asked, because I have structured five scientific yet simple protocols to take your performance through the roof. These protocols have been trench tested by me and the finest athletes Denmark has to offer. They are presented in chronological order, which is how I recommend they be followed (see Table 2).

Let's have a closer look at each protocol so you will know exactly what to do.

Table 2: Overview of the Complete Viking Warrior Conditioning Regime

Pay your dues with:	To test, stimulate, and peak:	For this amount of time:
The cMVO2 test	The snatch cadence that elicits a VO2max response.	Only once, before starting the 15:15 MVO2, the 36:36 MVO2, and the BOOST protocols.
The 15:15 MVO2 protocol	Your VO2max and work capacity while learning to snatch fast with an emphasis on overspeed eccentrics.	As long as it takes you to get to 80 sets of *at least* 7 reps per 15 seconds with your starting kettlebell (**Note: This is a minimum.**)
The 36:36 MVO2 protocol	1. Your VO2max along with your ability to buffer lactic acid (La) and other muscle metabolites. 2. Your anaerobic energy turnover. Your newly gained increases in your body's oxygen uptake. This is a peaking protocol for your VO2max.	As long as it takes to get you to 35 sets of *at least* 17 reps per 36 seconds with your starting kettlebell (**Note: This is a minimum.**)
The MVO2 BOOST protocol	Your newly gained increases in your body's oxygen uptake. This is a peaking protocol for your VO2max.	For about 3 weeks as the protocol outlines
The LaT protocol	Your lactic acid tolerance (LaT) ability. This is another crucial part of a complete conditioning program. Being able to tolerate high lactate levels means being able to perform with high power without fatigue.	For as long as it takes you to get to 1 minute x 15 sets of 130% to 150% your average 10-minute snatch test (SSST = Secret Service Snatch Test, or UST = Ultimate Snatch Test)
The MSLaP protocol	Your maximum speed (MS) and lactic acid production (LaP) ability. Being able to produce large amounts of lactate is a great indication of a well-conditioned anaerobic energy system.	For as long as the protocol outlines. Consider doing this simultaneously with another go at the 15:15 MVO2 protocol. Once or twice per week is recommended.

THE cMVO2 TEST

This protocol tests the specific cadence that elicits a VO2max response. It is based on a five-minute incremental test, in which the snatch cadence increases every minute. The starting weight is usually a 16 kg for men and a 12 kg for women. However, based on the cadence in the final minute of snatching, you might need to adjust the weight.

Breakdown

You will be switching hands on the minute, so consider which arm should go first. During the first four minutes of testing, it's very important that you keep the designated pace, instead of jumping the gun and cranking out the specified reps. The setup looks like this:

1st minute: 10 reps, or 1 rep per 6.0 seconds
2nd minute: 14 reps, or 1 rep per 4.2 seconds
3rd minute: 18 reps, or 1 rep per 3.3 seconds
4th minute: 22 reps, or 1 rep per 2.7 seconds
5th minute: All out, or as many reps as possible

Remember to count reps during this final minute, as you will need the number to figure out the interval snatch cadence during the 15:15, 36:36, and BOOST protocols.

When you are doing the test, don't be too concerned about hitting 1 rep per 4.2 seconds during the second minute. Just make sure you come close. For instance, during the second minute, I would think about hitting 2 reps every 9 seconds, evenly spaced out, which makes it a bit easier to keep the designated pacing. For the third minute, do 2 reps every 7 seconds, and for the fourth, do 2 reps every 5 seconds. Doing reps in this fashion enables you to test yourself, without having a partner calling the cadence.

For the fifth minute, do not cheat! Stop the second the timer beeps, and remember the number of snatches. That number corresponds to your cVO2max—the cadence that elicits a VO2max response.

If you get 24 reps or less during the fifth minute, you should grab a lighter kettlebell and do the test again when you have recovered. If you get 40 or more reps, you should grab a heavier kettlebell and do the test again on another day. If this happens, you should probably also consider if you are willing to look Pavel Tsatsouline in the eye when he asks you if all of those reps where RKC-style approved—meaning, did you lock out with the arm vertical?

The 15:15 MVO2 Protocol

The 15:15 MVO2 protocol is multiple sets of 15 seconds of snatching separated by 15 seconds of active rest. For each set, you need to keep your tested snatch cadence. The goal is to work up to 80 work sets of snatches before moving on to the 36:36 MVO2 protocol. The work:rest ratio is 1:1.

Breakdown

To get started with the 15:15 MVO2 protocol, divide your one-minute snatch cadence by 4 and round up. The result reflects how many snatches you need to do every set of 15 seconds.

Example

A person finishes the fifth minute of the test by doing 28 reps. Divide that number by 4, which equals 7. For each 15-second set of the 15:15 MVO2 protocol, the person needs to do 7 reps.

You can stay with the 15:15 MVO2 protocol for a long time. When you finally complete 80 sets of 9 reps per set, you will be forced either to move on or to grab a heavier kettlebell and start over. Personally, I recommend moving to the next level and starting the 36:36 MVO2 protocol. However, you should not start the next protocol until you are able to complete at least 80 sets of 7 reps.

The 36:36 MVO2 Protocol

The 36:36 MVO2 protocol is multiple sets of 36 seconds of snatching separated by 36 seconds of active rest. For each set, you need to keep your tested snatch cadence. The goal is to work up to 35 work sets of snatches before moving on to the MVO2 BOOST protocol. The work:rest ratio is still 1:1.

Breakdown

To get started with the 36:36 MVO2 protocol, divide your one-minute snatch cadence by 10, multiply by 6, and round it up. The result reflects how many snatches you need to do every set of 36 seconds.

Example

A person finishes the fifth minute of the test by doing 28 reps. Divide that number by 10, which equals 2.8 reps; then multiply by 6, which equals approximately 17 reps. For each 36-second set of the 36:36 MVO2 protocol, the person needs to do 17 reps.

During this protocol, many people ask why the interval setting is 36 seconds. They point out that 36 seconds is not very easy to time and suggest using 30 seconds on/off. My answer is that no, it cannot be 30 seconds on/off, because that is not the optimal time spent at VO2max for each interval. Thirty-six seconds is 60% of 1 minute. Research has shown that doing intervals at 60% of the time spent at VO2max is far superior to 50% (the suggestion of 30-second sets) or 70% or even 40% and 80% when doing high volume work (35 sets).

The answer to the timing problem is to get a Gymboss timer (go to www.kettlebells.dk).

The MVO2 Boost Protocol

After several months of using the 15:15 MVO2 and the 36:36 MVO2 protocols, it could very well be time to peak your conditioning. In addition, you will need something to prepare you for the LaT protocol to come. The MVO2 BOOST protocol will do exactly that. It's a 14-session peaking plan for your VO2max at supramaximal intensity, to be completed in about three weeks. During this time, you will need to reduce your strength practice.

Breakdown

The number of sets and work:rest ratio has been predetermined, so what you need to figure out is how fast you will be snatching and what size kettlebell to use. The cadence is determined by taking the cMVO2 test and adding 2 reps to your 15-second cadence. If the cadence is more than 9 or 10 reps per 15 seconds, you should grab a heavier kettlebell and do the cMVO2 test again.

Example

A person tests his or her VO2max cadence with the cMVO2 test and gets 26 reps the final minute. To determine the 15-second set cadence, divide 26 reps by 4, which is 6.5; then add 2, which makes 8.5 reps.

This number can be rounded either up or down. For this protocol, you should round it down if you are not going to increase the kettlebell size. So, 8 reps it is.

The MVO2 BOOST protocol calls for several 15-second sets and several 30-second sets. For the 30-second sets, just double your numbers from the 15-second sets.

In the example, the person will be hitting 8 reps per 15 seconds and 16 reps per 30 seconds.

Calculating the intensity

To calculate the intensity, use this formula:

MVO2 BOOST intensity = MVO2 BOOST cadence / cMVO2 test x 100

In the previous example, the numbers would look like this:

MVO2 BOOST intensity = 32 reps/min. / 26 reps/min. x 100 = 123% VO2max

The MVO2 BOOST protocol schedule

Sessions 1, 2, and 3:

3 x (15 sec. left + 15 sec. right), Rest 45 sec. +
3 x (30 sec. left + 30 sec. right), Rest 1½–2 min.

Sessions 4 and 5:

4 x (15 sec. left + 15 sec. right), Rest 45 sec. +
4 x (30 sec. left + 30 sec. right), Rest 1½–2 min.

Sessions 6, 7, and 8:

5 x (15 sec. left + 15 sec. right), Rest 45 sec. +
5 x (30 sec. left + 30 sec. right), Rest 1½–2 min.

Sessions 9, 10, and 11:

6 x (15 sec. left + 15 sec. right), Rest 45 sec. +
6 x (30 sec. left + 30 sec. right), Rest 1½–2 min.

Sessions 12, 13, and 14:

7 x (15 sec. left + 15 sec. right), Rest 45 sec. +
7 x (30 sec. left + 30 sec. right), Rest 1½–2 min.

Note that during each set, you will switch hands without putting the kettlebell down. You should complete all of the 30-second sets (15 sec. left + 15 sec. right) first and all of the 1-minute sets (30 sec. left + 30 sec. right) second.

THE LAT PROTOCOL

When you have paid your dues with the 15:15 MVO2 protocol, aced the 36:36 MVO2, and tackled the new MVO2 BOOST, you will have already embarked on a new journey in your Viking Warrior Conditioning. In addition to your goal of achieving the conditioning level of a true Viking Warrior, you will be striving for something called *cardiovascular specialized variety*. This focus on cardiovascular stimulation was initiated with the MVO2 BOOST protocol and will continue with this final protocol.

Enter the LaT protocol for upping your lactic acid tolerance (LaT)! Completing this protocol will give you the power of the Viking god Thor himself and take your SSST beyond the Gates of Valhalla.

Breakdown

For this protocol, take your best SSST or UST score and add 30% to 50%, depending on which interval your score is in:

- Less than 200 reps in 10 min. you should add 50%
- 200 – 215 reps in 10 min. you should add 45%
- 216 – 230 reps in 10 min. you should add 40%
- 231-245 reps in 10 min. you should add 35%
- More than 245 reps in 10 min. you should add 30%

Example

A person's cMOV2 test produced 24 reps/min. (Note that this test has to be done with the same kettlebell you are going to use for the protocol; otherwise, it will be difficult to calculate the intensity.) His SSST PR is 220 reps; 40% of 220 is 88. Adding 220 and 88 makes 308 reps. Divide 308 by 10 min. to get the cadence needed to achieve that score, and then round up. That cadence is approximately 31 reps/min. This is the person's cadence for the intervals in this protocol.

If this were your cadence, you would do a set of 31 reps within 1 minute and then rest for 2 minutes. The work:rest ratio is 1:2. If you can't do more than three sets before losing this cadence, you should increase the rest to 3 minutes and work from there, rather than decrease the reps per minute.

When you can do 15 sets, reduce the rest to 1.5 minutes, thus changing the work:rest ratio to 1:1½. When you can do 13 to 15 sets, you will be ready to retest your SSST/UST numbers and move on with the Viking Warrior Conditioning regime.

Calculating the intensity

The procedure is the same as for the MVO2 BOOST protocol:

LaT protocol intensity = LaT protocol cadence / cMVO2 test score x 100

In the above example, the numbers would look like this:

LaT protocol intensity = 31 reps/minute / 24 reps/minute x 100 = 130% VO2max

When doing longer sets (1 minute or more) and going at an overspeed cadence, it is not advisable to have a work:rest ratio of 1:1. The minimum should be 1:1½. This is to ensure that you can keep the specified cadence for a prolonged time and progress to a high workload (volume). Doing so is important not only because these are key concepts of cardiovascular stimulation with the kettlebell but also because the blood lactate level peaks after a hard set, not during.

✝HE MSLaP PROTOCOL

The final piece of the puzzle is the Maximum Speed Lactic Acid Production (MSLaP) protocol. During this protocol, you will primarily be working your body's ability to produce lactic acid. You will also continue to stimulate your ability to tolerate a high lactate level. To create these kinds of adaptations to your body, you must go at maximum speed.

This protocol also gives you the opportunity to increase the weight of the kettlebell by using the next size available. So, if you were using the 24 kg kettlebell for the LaT protocol, use the 28 kg or even the 32 kg kettlebell for this protocol.

Breakdown

The work:rest ratio is 1:6 or 1:10, meaning that you will rest for 6 to 10 times as long as your work set, depending on how long your work set is.

The MSLaP protocol calls for increasing the time you are working at your maximum snatch speed. To get started, doing 10-second sets is appropriate. During your first session, warm up thoroughly and start snatching your kettlebell of correct size as fast as possible. You still have to use valid RKC hard style, though, which means no cutting corners. Remember to count your repetitions.

After 10 seconds of maximum snatching, rest for 6 times as long. Then do the same thing again. Go as fast as possible for 10 seconds, and count your reps. The result will be one of three outcomes:

1. You manage more reps than in your previous set, which is fine. This new number will now be the goal for each set.
2. You manage exactly the same number of reps, which is also fine.
3. You do less than what you did in your first set. If this happens, double the duration of the rest break until you can do the same number of reps in the second set. You need at least two sets in your first session, which will provide you with a starting point.

> *Example*
> *A person is using a 32 kg kettlebell.*
> *1st set (10 seconds): 4 reps*
> > *Rest*
> *2nd set (10 seconds): 5 reps*
> > *Rest*
> *3rd set (10 seconds): 5 reps*
> > *Rest*
> *4th–9th sets (each 10 seconds): 5 reps*
> > *Rest*
> *10th set (10 seconds): 4 reps*

Doing 4 reps in the 10th set is an indication to stop the MSLaP protocol.

The number of sets to shoot for is 12. When you reach that number, start over and increase the duration of work to 20 seconds; the work:rest ratio will increase to 1:8. If you have been doing 5 reps per 10 seconds, you should now strive for doing 10 reps per 20 seconds and resting 2 min.:40 sec. When you can do 12 sets, add another 10 seconds to each set of snatches. Now you will be snatching for 30 seconds, hitting 15 reps, and resting 4 min.:30 sec., which is a work:rest ratio of 1:9. Repeat the cycle one more time and go for 40-second sets, hitting 20 reps and resting 6 minutes (work:rest ratio of 1:10) until you complete 12 sets.

During this protocol, be sure to make the best of the rest breaks; practice non–snatch related exercises and do some stretches. Keeping the body moving is crucial, and active recovery is definitely recommended.

Run this protocol simultaneously with the 15:15 MVO2 protocol. If you have never done the 15:15 MVO2, however, do not combine the two. One or two sessions per week is appropriate for the MSLaP protocol. If you are following the Viking Warrior Conditioning regime for four sessions per week, do this protocol every other session. If you are doing three Viking Warrior Conditioning sessions per week, do the MSLaP protocol in just one session.

See Table 3 for an overview of the MSLaP protocol.

Table 3: Overview of the MSLaP Protocol

Interval Work Duration	Rest (min:sec) Duration	Work: Rest Ratio	Number of Intervals	Kettlebell Cadence*	Kettlebell Size	Session Work: Rest Time
10 sec.	1:00	1:6	12	Maximum	1–2 sizes up	2min.:11min.
20 sec.	2:40	1:8	12	Maximum	Same	4min.:29min.
30 sec.	4:30	1:9	12	Maximum	Same	6min.:49min.
40 sec.	6:00	1:10	12	Maximum	Same	8min.:66min.

This protocol will work only if you are going as fast as you possibly can without holding anything back. This cannot be stressed enough.

RINSE AND REPEAT!

When you have successfully completed the 15:15 MVO2, 36:36 MVO2, BOOST, and LaT protocols, you should feel free to start all over again with a second run of the 15:15 MVO2. For the second time around, you should do the MSLaP protocol in conjunction with the 15:15 MVO2, and when it is time to move on to the 36:36 MVO2, you should be at the end of the MSLaP protocol.

You might be wondering how long you can continue to use the Viking Warrior Conditioning regime and what it's actually possible to achieve. Well, there are really no limits to what you can accomplish. For instance, Mark O. Madsen, RKC, peaked with the 15:15 MVO2 protocol before going to the 2008 Olympics in Beijing, doing 80 sets of 8 reps (32 reps/min. cMOV2 score) with a 24 kg kettlebell at a body weight of 80 kg. That equals 640 snatches in 20 minutes of actual work time. Now that is A LOT of power!

Fitting in the Other Piece of the Puzzle: Your Strength Practice

You should at least be maintaining your absolute strength while following the Viking Warrior Conditioning regime, so here are three suggestions on how to structure your weekly training. Who knows? You may even add a little extra poundage on your chosen lifts!

Suggestion 1

Based on three or four Viking Warrior Conditioning sessions per week:

Monday: Viking Strength Practice

Tuesday: Viking Warrior Conditioning

Wednesday: Off

Thursday: Viking Strength Practice (optional) + Viking Warrior Conditioning

Friday: Off

Saturday: Viking Warrior Conditioning

Sunday: Viking Warrior Conditioning (optional)

Suggestion 2

Based on two Viking Warrior Conditioning sessions per week:

Monday: Viking Strength Practice

Tuesday: Viking Warrior Conditioning

Wednesday: Off

Thursday: Viking Strength Practice

Friday: Viking Warrior Conditioning

Saturday: Viking Strength Practice (optional)

Sunday: Off

SUGGESTION 3

Based on three Viking Warrior Conditioning sessions per week:

Monday: Viking Strength Practice + Viking Warrior Conditioning

Tuesday: Off

Wednesday: Viking Strength Practice + Viking Warrior Conditioning

Thursday: Off

Friday: Viking Strength Practice + Viking Warrior Conditioning

Saturday: Off

Sunday: Off

CHOOSING A WEEKLY SCHEDULE

Suggestion 1 focuses on the Viking Warrior Conditioning and maintaining your base Viking strength, while Suggestion 2 leaves a little more room for developing your base strength at the cost of Viking Warrior Conditioning. Suggestion 3 is the setup you might know from Pavel's Rite of Passage program, which can be found in his book *Enter the Kettlebell!* This setup works very well, but you have to be careful that the accumulated fatigue from the strength work does not prevent you from following the Viking Warrior Conditioning regime. This is also something to be aware of when following the other suggestions, but Suggestion 3, especially, has the potential to interfere with your performance during the Viking Warrior Conditioning part.

A fourth suggestion would be to rotate cycles of strength practice and Viking Warrior Conditioning, but to exclude the strength work completely would be a mistake, in my opinion. Do at least one brief Viking base strength session per week to maintain your strength foundation.

My personal favorites are Suggestions 3 and 1: number 3 because it fits with being able to practice other skills on Tuesdays and Thursdays plus weekends, and number 1 because snatching for that amount of weekly volume is a surefire way to greatness!

Please note that when you are doing the MVO2 BOOST protocol, you should reduce your strength practice to a maintenance level of just one session per week, regardless of what schedule you have chosen to follow.

6
MEET THÓRÓLF

L et me introduce you to the Viking Thórólf, a 35-year-old kettlebell enthusiast who weighs 86 kg (190 lbs.) and has several months of kettlebell training under his belt. He is closing in on snatching the 24 kg kettlebell for 200 reps in 10 minutes, and he has pretty good baseline strength levels. He wants to start the Viking Warrior Conditioning regime and is ready to go head on with the five protocols.

Thórólf also plays sports twice a week, so he has chosen the weekly schedule in Suggestion 3. For his base strength work, he will do kettlebell military presses, pistols, and pull-ups. He aspires to take on the Beast Tamer challenge someday, so he wants to practice those lifts, as well.

Thórólf's Training Plan

The warm-up always consists of some swings, get-ups, and goblet squats focusing on technique. The warm up takes about 10 minutes.

Monday
- Kettlebell military presses
- Pull-ups
- Viking Warrior Conditioning

Tuesday
- Sport practice

Wednesday
- Pistols
- Viking Warrior Conditioning

Thursday
- Off

Friday
- Kettlebell military presses
- Pull-ups
- Viking Warrior Conditioning

Saturday
- Sport practice

Sunday
- Off

This is the general outline of Thórólf's training plan, but every week, his base strength exercises have to rotate. Doing only pistols once every week will not cut it, so the next week, pistols and pull-ups will switch places, and the week after that, pull-ups will switch places with military presses. This way, there will be a natural backing-off week every third week for each of the three base strength lifts.

Thórólf and the 15:15 MVO2 protocol

For Thórólf's first session, he tests his VO2max snatch cadence with the cMVO2 protocol after doing his base strength work. He ends up doing 28 reps for the final minute with the 16 kg kettlebell. After that, he rests for about five minutes while he computes his cadence for every 15 seconds of work during the 15:15 MVO2 protocol. He needs to hit 7 reps per 15 seconds. A good starting point for Thórólf is to do 20 to 30 sets of 7 reps for his first MVO2 session.

Thórólf starts, and everything is going well until the twenty-third set. Then, he feels that he is losing speed and has a hard time keeping the pace. He gets one more set and calls it a day, having done 24 sets of 7 reps.

The progression Thórólf follows for the 15:15 MVO2 protocol looks like this:

1st session: Does 24 sets of 7 reps

2nd session: Adds 15% of sets and does 28 sets (rounded up by 0.4 sets)

3rd session: Adds another 10% of sets and does 31 sets (rounded up by 0.2 sets)

4th session: Adds 20% of sets and does 37 sets (rounded down by 0.2 sets)

5th session: Repeats the cycle. Adds 15% to the 4th session and does 43 sets (rounded up by 0.45 sets)

6th session: Should have done 47 sets, a 10% increase, but backs off. Does 15 sets and feels good about stopping there.

At this point, two weeks of training have passed. By the beginning of the third week, Thórólf is ready to go again:

7th session: Does 47 sets (the number he was supposed to do in the 6th session)

8th session: Adds 15% and does 54 sets

9th session: Adds 10% and does 59 sets

At the end of this third week, Thórólf can definitely feel the volume catching up. He is tempted to continue adding sets by reducing the reps that he does first to 6 and eventually to 5 per set. This is the wrong approach for Thórólf to take, however. After giving it some thought, he realizes that the entire idea of VO2max training is to work at a cadence equal to or above 100% VO2max. If he drops 1 or 2 reps per set, the intensity will go down and he won't be working at the desired intensity level.

Instead of reducing the reps, Thórólf decides to make the fourth week of training a complete backing-off week. He still follows the template, but he does only 15 to 20 sets of the 15:15 MVO2 protocol, keeping the cadence at 7 reps per set, and he also cuts the volume in half on his strength work.

By the beginning of the fifth week, Thórólf is ready to go again:

13th session: Adds 10% to 59 sets and ends up doing 65 sets

14th session: Adds another 10% to 65 sets and ends up doing 71 sets

15th session: Is almost at the 80-sets marker but plays it safe and does only 35 sets (50% of his previous session of 71 sets)

16th session: Is mentally preparing himself for the 80 sets to come during this week. Decides to ramp up a bit from the previous session's 35 sets and does a strong 50 sets. Also backs off his base strength work to 50% volume.

17th session: This is it! Goes for 80 sets of 7 reps and nails it! Thórólf is stoked!

18th session: For this final session of the week, he works on base strength according to the schedule and only does what he feels like of snatching.

THE STRUCTURE OF THÓRÓLF'S FIRST 15:15 MVO2 CYCLE

Remember that the intensity is kept constant at 100% VO2max, so the only parameter being manipulated is the volume of each session. This is very basic cycling of volume. Note in Figure 3 how there is a build-up and a back-off followed by a super compensation for four peaks, leading up to the goal of 80 sets.

Figure 3: Thórólf's First 15:15 MVO2 cycle
6 week 15:15 MVO2 Cycle

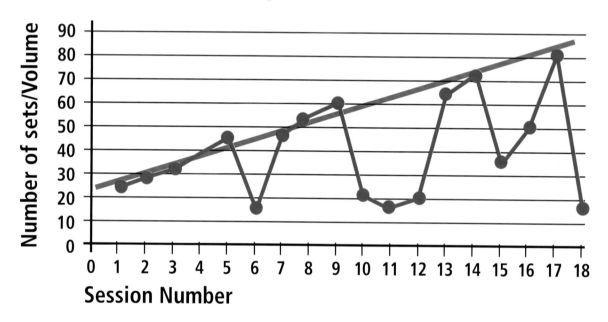

The dotted line indicates how the volume for the entire cycle develops. The gray line indicates the top volume for each week, which peaks at 80 sets.

At the start of the seventh week of training. Thórólf is ready to retest his VO2max cadence with the cMVO2 protocol and repeat the cycle. He hits 32 reps in the final minute of snatching, which equals a new VO2max cadence of 8 reps per 15 seconds. Thórólf will follow the same weekly structure, but this time, he will manipulate the intensity. He can't lower the intensity, but he can increase it. If 32 reps/min. equals 100% VO2max, then upping the cadence to 36 reps/min. will equal 112.5%. To work at that intensity for 15 seconds, Thórólf needs to hit 36 reps/min. divided by 4, or 9 reps/set, which is doable.

Topping 100% VO2max is referred to as going supramaximal, and doing it is really going to help Thórólf get to the next level of conditioning. So, in the following cycle, Wednesdays are going to be dedicated to supramaximal intensity snatching, with increasing contributions from the anaerobic energy system.

THE STRUCTURE OF THÓRÓLF'S SECOND 15:15 MVO2 CYCLE

Figure 4 shows the next eight weeks of Thórólf's 15:15 MVO2 training. Note again how it builds up, backs off, and supercompensates. This will get Thórólf ready for the next level, which is the 36:36 MVO2 protocol.

Figure 4: Thórólf's Second 15:15 MVO2 Cycle
8 week 15:15 MVO2 Cycle

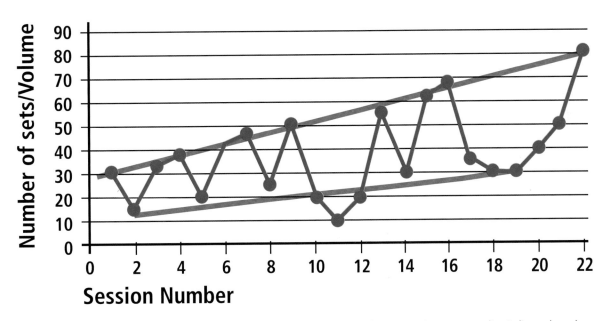

The dotted line reflects how the volume changes according to the session. The upper gray line indicates how the top volume for each week develops at 100% VO2max intensity. The lower gray line indicates how the volume develops at 112.5% VO2max intensity.

Thórólf embarks on the 36:36 MVO2 protocol

Thórólf is now ready to start the 36:36 MVO2 protocol. He tests his VO2max cadence with the 16 kg kettlebell and does 36 reps in the final minute. That cadence equals approximately 22 reps per set of the 36:36 protocol. Thórólf feels he is in a predicament, because that kind of cadence, going at an average of 9 reps/15 seconds, is getting close to impossible for sets of 36 seconds, if he wants to keep every rep clean, crisp, and hard style. Thórólf decides to try a cMVO2 test with the 20 kg kettlebell and see how that goes. After resting for 10 to 15 minutes, he gets 28 reps in the final minute with the 20 kg kettlebell. That brings him to a cadence of 17 reps per set for the 36:36 MVO2 protocol. Situation: excellent!

Now, Thórólf starts his journey toward 35 sets of 17 reps with the 20 kg kettlebell. He uses the same kind of cycling he used for the 15:15 MVO2 protocol, meaning that he builds up, backs off, and supercompensates until he is where he wants to be. Thórólf runs through the 36:36 MVO2 protocol twice. The second time, he hits 19 reps per set, and he eventually reaches 35 sets.

Thórólf's physique has changed dramatically. He is now more ripped than ever, and in terms of performance, he is in the best shape of his life. He has added more than 8 inches to his standing vertical jump, he is running a 100 m sprint in less than 12 seconds, and his body fat percentage is a single digit. He is ready to conquer the world!

Giving Thórólf a BOOST

Thórólf wants to peak his VO2max, so he starts the MVO2 BOOST protocol. During this time, he reduces his base strength practice to a bare minimum of just one brief session per week. He tests his VO2max cadence with the 20 kg bell and gets 33 reps. The MVO2 BOOST protocol calls for dividing his snatch cadence by 4 and adding 2 reps to that, bringing him to 10.25 reps per 15 seconds and 20.5 reps per 30 seconds.

Thórólf will most likely not be able to go that fast, so he decides to step up and do the test over again with the 24 kg kettlebell. He ends up snatching the 24 kg kettlebell for 22 reps during the final minute of testing, which is OK for this protocol, because he will be adding 2 reps per 15 seconds. That means that Thórólf's cadence is 22 reps/min. divided by 4, which is about 5.5. Adding 2 makes 7.5 reps per 15 seconds and 15 reps per 30 seconds.

Going to 24 kg is a pretty big jump in weight, so Thórólf decides to play it safe and rounds the numbers down instead of up. Doing so brings him to 14 reps per 30 seconds and 28 reps per minute.

Thórólf is now ready to start the MVO2 BOOST protocol. Here's how it goes down:

1st session:	3 x (15 sec. + 15 sec.), Rest 45 sec. + 3 x (30 sec. + 30 sec.), Rest 1½–2 min.
	3 x (7 reps + 7 reps), Rest 45 sec. + 3 x (14 reps + 14 reps), Rest 1½–2 min.
2nd session:	3 x (7 reps + 7 reps), Rest 45 sec. + 3 x (14 reps + 14 reps), Rest 1½–2 min.
3rd session:	3 x (7 reps + 7 reps), Rest 45 sec. + 3 x (14 reps + 14 reps), Rest 1½–2 min.
4th session:	4 x (7 reps + 7 reps), Rest 45 sec. + 4 x (14 reps + 14 reps), Rest 1½–2 min.
5th session:	4 x (7 reps + 7 reps), Rest 45 sec. + 4 x (14 reps + 14 reps), Rest 1½–2 min.
6th session:	5 x (7 reps + 7 reps), Rest 45 sec. + 5 x (14 reps + 14 reps), Rest 1½–2 min.
7th session:	5 x (7 reps + 7 reps), Rest 45 sec. + 5 x (14 reps + 14 reps), Rest 1½–2 min.
8th session:	5 x (7 reps + 7 reps), Rest 45 sec. + 5 x (14 reps + 14 reps), Rest 1½–2 min.
9th session:	6 x (7 reps + 7 reps), Rest 45 sec. + 6 x (14 reps + 14 reps), Rest 1½–2 min.
10th session:	6 x (7 reps + 7 reps), Rest 45 sec. + 6 x (14 reps + 14 reps), Rest 1½–2 min.
11th session:	6 x (7 reps + 7 reps), Rest 45 sec. + 6 x (14 reps + 14 reps), Rest 1½–2 min.
12th session:	7 x (7 reps + 7 reps), Rest 45 sec. + 7 x (14 reps + 14 reps), Rest 1½–2 min.
13th session:	7 x (7 reps + 7 reps), Rest 45 sec. + 7 x (14 reps + 14 reps), Rest 1½–2 min.
14th session:	7 x (7 reps + 7 reps), Rest 45 sec. + 7 x (14 reps + 14 reps), Rest 1½–2 min.

VOLUME PROGRESSION FOR THE BOOST PROTOCOL

A closer look at the intensity reveals why this protocol is going to give Thórólf a boost, as well as prepare him for the LaT protocol to come (see Figure 5). The intensity is calculated like this:

Intensity = Protocol snatch pace / cMVO2 score x 100

Punching in the numbers, Thórólf determines his intensity:

28 reps/min. / 22 reps/min. x 100 = 128% MVO2

Thórólf is at 128% intensity—perfectly stimulating his maximum oxygen uptake and increasing his anaerobic energy turnover by stimulating his ability to tolerate high levels of blood lactate. Now, it's time to move on to the LaT protocol.

Figure 5: MVO2 Volume Boost Progression

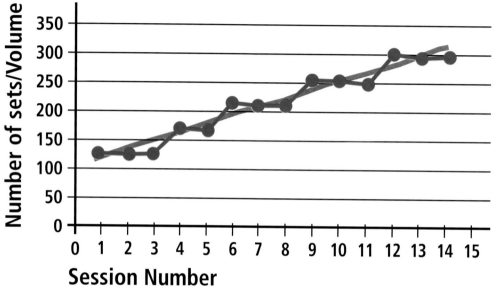

Like the 15:15 MVO2 and the 36:36 MVO2 protocols, the progression in the BOOST protocol is simple: Increase the volume and peak. Note that the difference between this and the two other protocols is that there are no back-off sessions. The volume steadily increases toward the peak. This approach works for several reasons: (1) the total volume is lower; (2) the density is reduced, which means the rest between sets is longer (this reduces the accumulated fatigue); and (3) the protocol is over in about three weeks.

The LaT protocol in effect

Thórólf decides to give the SSST another go, so he rests up until he is completely recovered. Then he cranks out 230 reps in 10 minutes with the 24 kg kettlebell at a bodyweight of 78 kg. It's time for Thórólf to embark on the LaT protocol to up his lactic acid tolerance. He also tests his VO2max cadence with the cMVO2 test on a separate day using the 24 kg kettlebell. He gets 25 reps the final minute, which equals 3 reps more than in the previous cMVO2 test.

Thórólf computes his numbers for the LaT protocol with the 24 kg kettlebell:

SSST score = 230 reps

40% of SSST score = 92 reps

Cadence required = (230 reps + 92 reps) / 10 = Approx. 32 reps/min.

Let's do a little math to figure out Thórólf's intensity level. During the LaT protocol, he will be snatching at an overspeed cadence of 32 reps/min. Calculating the intensity looks like this:

32 reps/min. / 25 reps/min. x 100 = 128% VO2max

This means Thórólf will be going 28% faster than what equals his maximum oxygen uptake.

To really stimulate the body's lactic acid tolerance, reaching an intensity of more than 120% VO2max is required. So, by calculating the intensity in this way, you can determine if you are working the correct combination of energy systems. The days of guessing whether you are doing it correctly are over! The numbers will reveal the truth.

If Thórólf is not content with a 128% VO2max intensity level, he has two options: (1) add more than the prescribed percentage to his SSST score and do more reps per set, or (2) grab a heavier kettlebell. Each option is valid for cycling into the training periodization, but neither is really necessary if the next protocol to be applied is the MSLaP protocol.

This will greatly tap Thórólf's anaerobic energy turnover while still stimulating his VO2max. With this protocol, Thórólf can have his cake and eat it, too. Until reaching an intensity level of about 160%, the VO2max will be stimulated along with the lactic acid tolerance, provided that a sufficient amount of volume and appropriate rest breaks are applied.

Adding the MSLaP protocol to a second run of the 15:15 MVO2

Thórólf is now ready to start over again with the 15:15 MVO2 protocol. He also adds the MSLaP protocol once a week. He still needs to take the cMVO2 test to establish a starting point for the 15:15 MVO2. He decides to do the test with the 24 kg kettlebell and to break out the 32 kg for the MSLaP. Thórólf is on the path to achieving extraordinary cardiovascular strength and endurance.

What about Thórólf's base strength?

Well, Thórólf's base strength is another story and beyond the scope of this book. I can tell you, though, that he attacked his strength work with great dedication and attention to detail. He continued to follow basic RKC principles and was getting closer to the BEAST Tamer Hall of Fame. Go Thórólf!

Wrapping up the story of Thórólf's training

Even though Thórólf is a fictitious character, the progress he's made can be entirely real for anyone with the dedication to follow the same training regime. Results like Thórólf's cannot be guaranteed, because where you end up will be based on your starting point, your genetic potential, and your work ethic. Regardless, I have witnessed several people transform themselves during the course of this training regime, and I have heard tons of success stories from people using this approach in their training.

One of those stories comes from Mark Reifkind, Master RKC and strength coach extraordinaire. Besides Danish Greco-Roman wrestler Mark O. Madsen, RKC, Reifkind has stuck with the Viking Warrior Conditioning regime the longest and has had great success with it in terms of improving cardiovascular power and capacity and body composition.

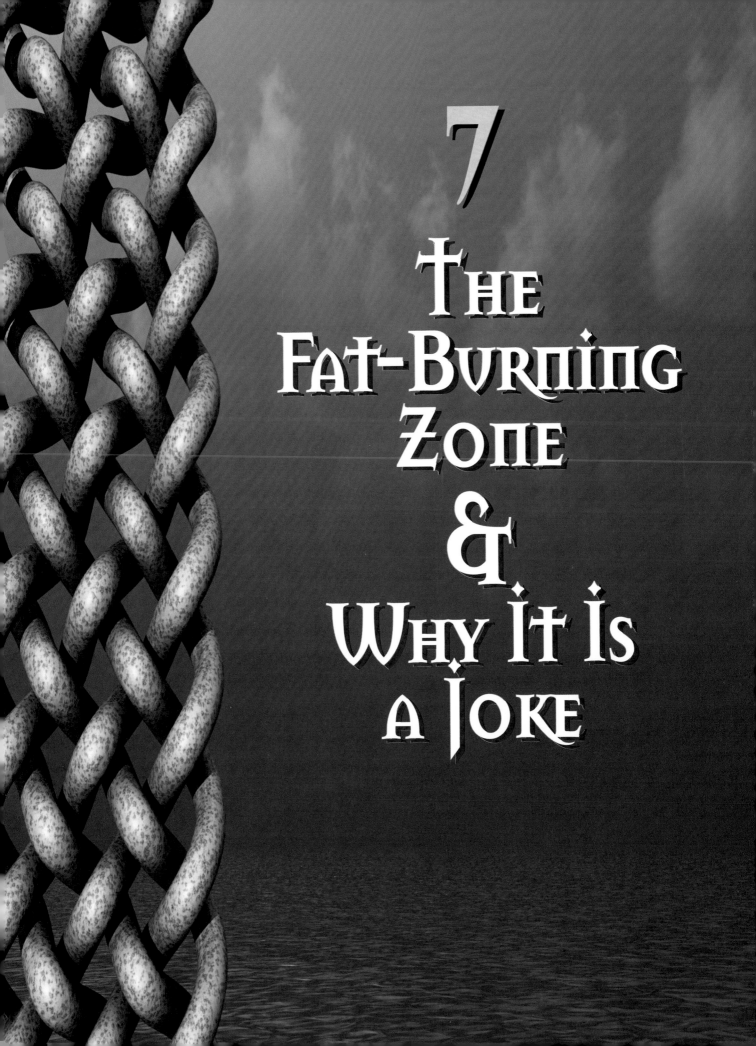

7
The
Fat-Burning
Zone
&
Why It Is
a Joke

INTERVAL TRAINING VERSUS STEADY STATE

First of all, the discussion of steady state versus interval training and which is better is pointless unless you understand energy turnover in the body and the meaning of intensity. This is about your VO2max, because when doing cardiovascular exercise, the amount of energy used for the activity is defined by the oxygen uptake.

This is best explained by a little math: One liter (l) of oxygen used by your muscles fuels the burn of approximately 20 kilojoules (kj). If you work for 20 minutes with an average oxygen consumption of 3.5 l/min., you will burn 1,400 kj, or approximately 330 kilocalories (kcal), calculated as follows:

3.5 l/min. x 20kj/l x 20 min. = 1,400 kj

This calculation is indisputable and has been known to be accurate since August Krogh, back in 1920s, did some of the first experiments on oxygen uptake. In the example above, if the person has a VO2max of 6 liters per minute, the intensity will be 3.5 l/min. divided by 6 l/min. times 100, or 58%, which is considered low to very low. On the other hand, if the person has a VO2max of 3.6 liters per minute, the intensity will be 3.5 l/min. divided by 3.6 l/min. times 100, or 97%, which is considered high. When talking about steady state versus intervals, you have to define at what intensity the work is being done.

A LITTLE MORE MATH

A person has a VO2max of 4.0 liters per minute and goes for a steady state run for 15 minutes at 95% of VO2max. This means that during the session, he will burn 1,140 kj, which equals 271 kcal, during those 15 minutes:

95% x 4.0 l/min. x 20 kj/l x 15 min. = 1,140 kj

On another day, this person does intervals for 15 minutes with an average intensity of 95% of his VO2max. The math on this is the same: He will burn 1,140 kj, or 271kcal.

The amount of kilojoules burned during a session is related to the *intensity* of the work being done, not directly to the *type* of work being done!

Is interval training better?

Why is it, then, that interval training seems to be so much better? The answer is simple.

When performing intervals, you can work at a higher percentage of your VO2max for short bursts, and when you are doing a lot of sets of short bursts, the average intensity will increase. You will also realize at this point just how important it is to have the correct work:rest ratio. If the rest period becomes too long compared to the duration of the work set, the average intensity of the entire session will drop. This is, of course, related to the VO2 kinetics explained previously.

Comparing two scenarios

Let's say that a normal person is able to work continuously at 85% VO2max for 25 minutes straight and then can't do any more (submaximal work). This means that if the person has a VO2max of 4.0 liters per minute, he or she will burn 1,700 kj (405 kcal) during those 25 minutes.

If the same person does the 15:15 MVO2 protocol for 40 sets at 120% VO2max (supramaximal work), the total time spent will be 20 minutes, including rest (10 minutes of actual work). He or she will burn 1,920 kj (457 kcal):

$$120\% \times 4.0 \text{ l/min.} \times 20 \text{ kj/l} \times 20 \text{ min.} = 1{,}920 \text{ kj}$$

So basically, this person is burning more calories in much less actual working time as well as total time.

In addition, working at a supramaximal intensity will have a greater stimulatory effect on type II muscle fibers compared to working at submaximal intensity. The postoxygen consumption, or *afterburn*, will also be greater. Lastly but equally important, the stimulatory effects on the heart are also greater when doing maximal and supramaximal work.

The infamous fat-burning zone

The much discussed fat-burning zone, which is often recommended by ignorant fitness professionals, calls for steady state work at 60% to 70% of the maximum heart rate (HRmax), which equals an intensity of 40% to 58% VO2max. If the amount of kilojoules burned is related to the intensity of the work, there is simply no good reason for doing exercise with an intensity that low.

The ACSM recommends an intensity level of at least 55% VO2max for making any cardiovascular adaptations, and this applies to individuals who never ever do any type of exercise other than get the Rocky Road Triple-Chunk Chocolate ice-cream out of the fridge.

The rationale behind the concept of the fat-burning zone comes from experiments on substrate choice during exercise at various intensities. Since the process of turning fat deposits into energy in the form of ATP is slow compared to the conversion of carbohydrates, the idea of the fat-burning zone suggests that by keeping the intensity low, the body will have enough time to convert the fat into energy and spare the carbohydrate deposits (glycogen).

To lose weight, there must be an energy deficit. If more energy is consumed than is needed to maintain a given lifestyle, the body will store the extra energy primarily as fat. This is termed a *positive energy balance*. If the energy intake during the day is less than required, the body will have an energy deficit and take the missing kilojoules from fat tissue storage. This is termed a *negative energy balance*.

Let's compare two simple workouts to determine which is best for the person who wants to lose weight.

WORKOUT I:
THE FAT-BURNING ZONE WORKOUT

Type of exercise: Running slowly for a long distance

Duration: 1 hour

Intensity: 70% HRmax = 58% VO2max

VO2max: 3.0 l/min.

VO2 during work: 1.74 l/min.

Energy spent: 1.74 l/min. x 20 kj/l x 60 min.

= 2,088 kj = 497 kcal

WORKOUT 2: THE HIGH-INTENSITY WORKOUT

Type of exercise: 15:15 MVO2 interval sprints

Duration: 80 sets = 40 min. (Actual work time = 20 min.)

Intensity: 95% VO2max (average for session including rest)

VO2max: 3.0 l/min.

VO2: 2.85 l/min.

Energy spent: 2.85 l/min. x 20 kj/l x 40 min. = 2,280 kj = 542 kcal

DIFFERENCES BETWEEN THE TWO WORKOUTS

When comparing the two workouts, two things stand out:

1. The total amount of kilojoules spent is greater in Workout 2.

2. The time it takes to complete Workout 2 is two-thirds that of Workout 1, and the actual work time of Workout 2 is one-third that of Workout 1. If we match the two workouts in duration, so that Workout 2 is also one hour in duration, the energy spent will be 3,420 kj (814 kcal), which is 64% more than that of Workout 1. Plus, the actual work time of Workout 2 will be just 30 minutes.

OTHER NOT SO OBVIOUS DIFFERENCES

While the numbers speak for themselves, we also have to consider the stimulatory effect of each workout on the heart. If the heart is not pushed close to the VO2max, the adaptation of the heart chambers will not be significant. During Workout 1, only a little eccentric hypertrophy will occur; that means the VO2max will increase an insignificant amount. During Workout 2, the intensity is high enough to stimulate eccentric hypertrophy of the heart, resulting in an increase in VO2max. If the VO2max increases, for instance, to 3.5 l/min., then the VO2 during Workout 2 will increase from 2.85 l/min. to 3.33 l/min.—further increasing the energy spent to a whopping 2,660 kj, or 633 kcal, for a 40-minute workout.

In addition, going fast with high-acceleration force stimulates the type II muscle fibers to a greater extent than is possible with a low-intensity, steady state workout. This will result in an increase in the rate of force development. And finally, if we look closer at what is going on at the cellular level, metabolic markers such as HAD, CS, PFK, CK, and the like will also increase to a greater extent, which will basically turn up your metabolism for an even greater fat burn. Scientists have con-

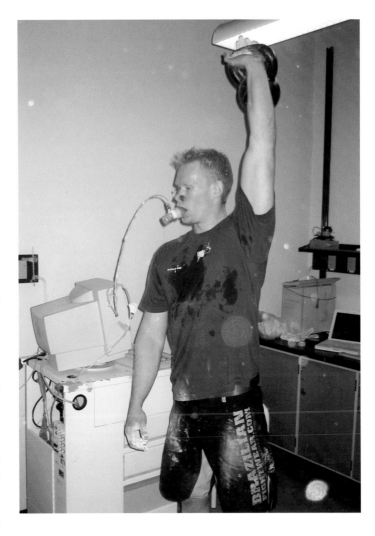

cluded that "by using explosive contractions and moderate exercise intensity, experienced recreational exercisers can increase their energy expenditure during and after resistance exercise, and this could enhance weight-loss adaptations."

So, to make it simple, just say NO to the fat-burning zone and do things hard style, like a Viking!

8
✝ THE TRIPOD
OF
CONDITIONING

he term *conditioning* relates to various aspects of a training program. In this section, I will provide you with an example of how you can interpret *conditioning* in relation to the development of the all-round athlete.

LET'S BREAK IT DOWN

The size of the triangle in Figure 6 reflects the level of conditioning, and just as three sides make up a triangle, three baseline factors determine the level of conditioning. Those three factors are (in no particular order) oxygen uptake (VO2), metabolite production ability, and metabolite tolerance ability. All three factors are interconnected and influence one another, depending on how they are developed through the structure of training.

Figure 6: The Tripod of Conditioning

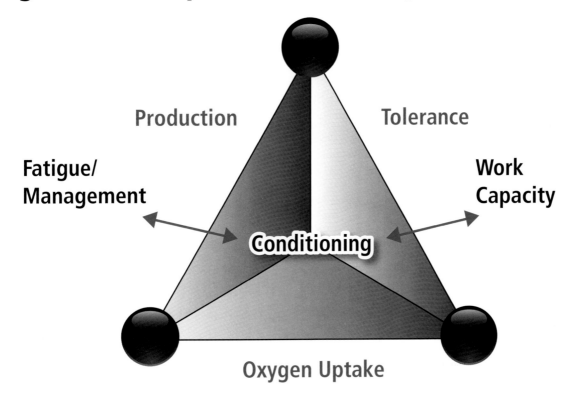

The tripod of conditioning illustrates that three factors—oxygen uptake, metabolite production ability, and metabolite tolerance ability—indicate the level of conditioning. Outside factors like fatigue, fatigue management, and work capacity can be limiting as well as the parameters used for measuring improvement.

OXYGEN UPTAKE ABILITY

Your oxygen uptake ability is basically a measure of how well your cardiovascular system is able to transport and utilize oxygen. Having a good oxygen update ability is important for two reasons: (1) you will be able to work at a higher intensity before having to recruit the anaerobic energy system significantly, and (2) your recovery will go faster, because a well-conditioned cardiovascular system is better at getting rid of anaerobic by-products than a less well-conditioned cardiovascular system.

METABOLITE PRODUCTION ABILITY

Depending on the intensity of your training session, you will tap the anaerobic energy turnover system to some degree. When the anaerobic energy system provides energy in the form of ATP, it is done through two different pathways: the alactic acid system and the lactic acid system.

The *alactic acid system* is always the first to kick in (after you use the little ATP already available in the muscle—about 1 to 2 seconds' worth), and energy will be produced by dissociating creatine phosphate (PCr). The *lactic acid system* is based on how well your body can transform carbohydrates (glucose and glycogen) into ATP, forming lactic acid as a by-product. If that system is fast, it will quickly transform carbohydrates into the energy the body needs. As a consequence, a lot of metabolites will also be formed, including lactate, hydrogen ions, and extracellular potassium. These metabolites will eventually build up, provided that the intensity is sufficient, and ultimately cause you to stop exercising and rest until levels have returned to normal.

METABOLITE TOLERANCE ABILITY

The more your body is able to tolerate high levels of metabolites (lactic acid), the longer you will be able to go before being forced to stop exercise. Consider this simple example: Two persons who are exactly the same except for their ability to tolerate lactic acid are doing the same exercise at the same intensity. One person can tolerate 24 millimoles of lactate acid, and the other can tolerate only 15 millimoles of lactate acid. This means that the first person will be able to continue the exercise for a longer time before having to stop.

OUTSIDE FACTORS

Fatigue, along with the ability to manage it, is a huge factor in the general conditioning of the body. Too little rest combined with fatigue will cause you to stop what you are doing. Too much rest will diminish what you are trying to accomplish in your conditioning. That's why it is of the utmost importance to structure your training sessions with the correct work:rest ratio.

There are different kinds of fatigue, and I will not go into detail about them. But in this context, let's say that fatigue represents the acute response to a training session.

Fatigue is, in general, not very well understood. However, a good amount of research indicates that local factors in the working muscles are mostly responsible for the development of fatigue. The extracellular build-up of potassium is considered one possible culprit because of an inhibition of the nerve impulse (action potential) to the muscle. The accumulation of hydrogen ions, which dissociate from lactate, is also considered as a factor; it lowers the pH value in the environment around the muscle and turns it acidic, causing the muscle cross-bridge cycle to stop working. Factors like temperature will also cause fatigue. If the body's core temperature reaches about 40.5 degrees Celsius, the person will stop exercising.

Put simply, when doing any kind of cardiovascular training, the management of fatigue is extremely important. Too much rest, and your results will suffer. Too little rest, and you will have to stop prematurely.

Fatigue is, of course, also an issue when freestyling the training. By *freestyling*, I mean mixing strength work with conditioning. This approach requires you to be very smart about what exercises and set/rep/rest schemes you choose. Freestyling can be done successfully, however, and for those people who cannot plan ahead in detail, it's a very good option.

Do not overlook the impact of fatigue on your conditioning. By staying clear of excessive fatigue while making sure you are not resting too much, you will optimize the outcome of your training.

Your work capacity goes hand in hand with your ability to manage fatigue. Too much fatigue, and your work capacity is reduced. Looking at the tripod of conditioning (see Figure 6), it should be evident that when the conditioning level increases, the work capacity increases, as well. Being able to tolerate higher levels of metabolites, being able to produce more metabolites at a higher rate, and increasing the VO2max will increase your ability to work for a longer duration at a higher intensity. Who doesn't want that?

The complete picture— the tripod of power

So far, we have only addressed the conditioning aspect of general training, but it's important to remember that we can look at power in a similar fashion, with the same outside factors affecting it. To complete the picture, let's look at the general power component (see Figure 7).

Figure 7: The Tripod of Power

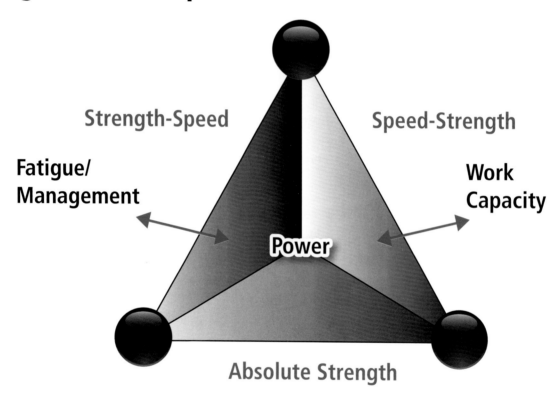

The tripod of power illustrates that three factors influence power development: the absolute strength base (1RM), along with the strength-speed and speed-strength. Strength-speed and speed-strength are both components of explosive strength (RFD). The higher the levels of these three factors, the more power it will be possible to generate in any given instant. Outside factors like fatigue, fatigue management, and work capacity will influence and be affected by the development of each of the three tripod components.

THE ULTIMATE GOAL

The ultimate goal—at least for people who are not doing acyclical activities like powerlifting and shot putting—is achieved by combining the two tripods: the tripod of conditioning and the tripod of power. When they are combined, the result is power–endurance, which is destined to lead to increased performance in any cyclical activity. If you are a martial artist; in the military; a police officer or firefighter; a rugby, football, soccer, basketball, volleyball, handball, lacrosse, or tennis player; or someone who just wants to look strong, trim, and toned in a bathing suit, combining the two tripods should be your goal. A high level of power–endurance, with a work capacity and ability to manage fatigue to match, will bring success.

9

Testaments to the Power of Viking Warrior Conditioning

The snatch and I have danced under many moons, to many tunes.

The Snatch. The Tsar of kettlebell lifts. "Fluid and vicious" is how The Evil Russian expressed it in the book.

"Fluid and vicious" is an appropriate description of the contents of my stomach, nearly on their way out, after my first attempt to snatch a weight overhead. I was aboard the USS *Peleliu* as a young Marine wog. I had read an article in the late, great publication *Muscle Media*, authored by Pavel, detailing the parameters of a snatch. I had never snatched a barbell or seen a kettlebell, and I had rarely pressed a single arm over my head. I had pressed barbells and pairs of dumbbells, cables, infrequently, but not often with a single appendage, nor had I oriented all of my lifts from the hips.

Upon trying, I lacked the development in my stabilizer muscles to properly lock the awkward, rusty, hex-dumbbell into place. I did, however, take the advice of The Russian and use a lighter weight than I had been pressing. I walked into my future with a 40 pound weight, and upon terminating the set on my right arm at 10 reps, I thought I was going to vacate the chow in my stomach. It was 2100 hours, the ship was in high seas, and I was way out of my element.

The snatch and I share an interesting history. Not only was it the first ballistic exercise that I ever attempted, but it was the drill that I practiced to commune with a hard-style instructor base. Regular bouts with repetition snatching arrived in the summer of 2003, with my foolishly throwing up a dumbbell yet soon snatching a kettle stack in my apartment in Vegas while watching *The Russian Kettlebell Challenge* on VHS.

I repped out at the First National Kettlebell Convention Secret Service Snatch Test with a studly 202 repetitions. I hammered a two-pood for a triple-one in front of a Philly RKC. The snatch and I have danced under many moons, to many tunes.

I have followed few snatch programs in my day that are worth mentioning. I developed the disposable directives. The most effective guidelines were those from the *Soviet Weightlifting Yearbook* that Pavel outlines in *The Russian Kettlebell Challenge* book. There's also a 10-minute Secret Service Snatch Test protocol delivered to me by Rob Lawrence. And then there's our chorus of castigation, the VO2max regime—singularly, the 15:15.

Snatching brings the user a specified bushel of pain. The shredded hands, the brutalized hamstrings, and the deep, nearly spiritual soreness that come from high-rep snatching are details of training that could be sung around a dozen campfires. Be it the coveted Master of Sports ranking in Soviet GS or the hard-styler's delight in the SSST, we choose to walk the line knowing the tar will get beat out of us before we see it through.

I have read that skateboarders revel in the fruits of a day spent rolling city streets, tearing up curbs and giant planters, searching for a tasty patch of urbanography to trick out, leading to sore calves and backs, ripped denim, braised skin, and lost ball caps. Surfers, who spend entire nights waking periodically to check the online reports, tell tales of deep muscle soreness attributed to facing down dozens of sets, out there in the sea, digging for the finest waves, in the meatiest spots the coast has to offer each morning. Screaming quads, aching shoulder girdles from repeated paddle-outs, and the exhausted internal battery that fuels the passion for what they do are markers of a young grom's efforts. Tribal, territorial, thorough.

As New School Gireviks, we are also tribal, clans banded together under the high quotient of competent leadership nurturing a vision. Territorial? We mark our neighborhoods' best outdoor kettlebelling corners with videos posted on the web and bloggings detailing the daily due. Thorough, as well, we need the details on how to best snatch and best press the fastest and the heaviest. We achieve a bountiful reward by focusing on the fewest aspects.

Skaters patrol the city and surfers cruise the coastlines, so naturally, a hard-styler's home is the field, the park, the rooftop. How many times have you set out for an outdoor session and torn up your calluses and posterior muscles with high-rep snatches? If you are anything like me, those days are endless in number and recorded forever in the annals.

On those days, however, I often fragged myself. I charged the hill with too much vigor. I lost training time because my plan was poor. "Snatch often, snatch heavy," Chesty would decree. "Now, snatch till you can no longer," as the nameless external motivators would have me believe. And I believed! I believed until that misguided gusto, paired with residual pain from multiple motor vehicle accidents, landed me in the chiro's office in the winter of 2006.

When I recovered from treatment and was rested enough, I undertook Rob Lawrence's SSST protocol for improving my 10-minute/1.5-pood placement. Following the protocol until its end, I then did myself, and Rob, a disservice by not retesting my 10-minute, 24 kg numbers. Zealously, I did my own thing and launched into an operation designed to improve my 5-minute/2-pood ranking. After taking Rob's math and my arrogance, I bitch-slapped my old total by 19 reps and, witnessed by a Philly RKC, emptied the clip with 111 reps in 5 minutes. A 32 kg death march.

I broke from snatching altogether until that fiery day at Dayton's Bluff in June 2007, when The Dane of Pain went insane and dropped his VO2max cadence test and 15:15 protocol on the unsuspecting Level II student body.

The idea of a four-minute snatch cadence, followed by one minute of all-out repping to establish your magic number, sounded evil. A 30-set minimum sounded nastier than your average kettlebell workout. And when the Dane set the number of sets for peaking at 80, I nearly called the airport shuttle service and left the state. Standing next to fellow Senior RKC Doug Nepodal (both of us then serving as sergeants), representing with 24 kilograms, I crushed the cMOV2 test and ended up with 33 snatches on the final minute. My number was 8.

I took this training home with me to Philadelphia and sucker-punched my next two kettlebell classes with a cMOV2 and 20-set "sampler." Later in the week, I marched a few clients to the plank and chortled at the splash.

I rambled through a six-week cycle of 15:15, and when I wrapped, the 24 kg kettlebell was feeling light. Crazy light! It was summertime in Pennsylvania, and snatching in humid conditions with slippery hands and sucking thick, bug-busy air had made a man out of me.

Switching my training up to a hypertrophy stage saw me part ways with the 15:15 until we met again in Denmark in '08. Master RKC Mark Reifkind, along with Tracy Reifkind, maintained excellent blogs that detailed their travels through the land of 15:15. By the time I got to DK, Rif and T-Rif's daily-refreshed reports detailed their experience with training VO2max accurately, so that all I felt was left to do was to start digging. It appeared that the full cycle would build the endurance it claimed. Fifty, 60, and upward to 80 sets would arrive at the hard-styler's doorstep if he or she just kept snatching. There was no fear that experience with high-rep snatching in the past, leading to burnt palms and a twisted wreck of a neck, would derail me. The weight of the kettlebell was not relevant to one's bodyweight, provided that the focused eccentric overspeed was in place on every rep.

Viewing the training blogs of Rif and T-Rif and having twice seen The Dane in VO2 form provided me with the guts and a cognitive craving for the day when would I stand atop the kettlebell, victorious. The day when 80 sets were smashed and cashed like I had swung Thor's hammer down into the most deafening of dark places.

Sets of 15:15 crept into my week between the RKC Denmark and a special training event at the U.S. Marines' Base Camp Pendleton. Tasked with administering the VO2max 15:15 to a small group at a closed RKC event on Camp Pen, I explored the cMVO2 with a 16 kg. My number again was 8. Two weeks later, I stood online with my team at RKC UCLA and snatched in sync with commands from The Dane. My number with 16 kg again was 8. Nothing in recent memory has felt as familial as snatching alongside those candidates, knowing that my at-bat may have driven them further and my sets may have given them hope.

Watching Kenneth, taller than me, move the bell along its tamed arc with speed and ferocity brought me to a new level of comprehension. I knew that adjustments to my form had to be made to hit 80 sets without losing training time to injury. Suffering was imminent, but damage was preventable. The clearest understanding of the very best protocol that hard-style snatching has to offer had finally been driven home. And with 80 sets of 15:15 under my belt as I write this, the purest child of third-way "hybrid cardio" has given me a heart of elastic steel, built to shift gears and keep my wheels spinning faster than the other guy can process. I bear a lower body fat percentile than I have maintained in a few years. And I come heavily armed, clad in a defensive suit drawn of flesh, with two palms conditioned to pull for high reps under the grizzliest of conditions. Like a Viking, indeed.

VO2max Profitable Roll Call

⊙ The size of the kettlebell is not terribly relevant, due to the emphasis on overspeed eccentrics, allowing for a low-weight/high-volume aerobic protocol to yield substantial gains and to give trainees with an aversion to heavy kettlebells a chance to train hard and potentially free of neck, shoulder, or back problems.

⊙ At the turnover, where lockout becomes an active spike, the contraction of the latissimus dorsi has brought about noticeable changes in the loaded cleans I practice prior to a press.

⊙ Save for the initial cMVO2 testing, there has been zero delayed onset muscle soreness worthy of report. My strength training has not suffered in any manner.

⊙ Using the cMVO2 workouts to enhance the grip or protect the palms is optimal. Sock sleeves or sweatbands may be used either to protect the skin of the palms or to beef up the grip with some added difficulty. The sets are short enough that one may actually get to his or her full 80 sets of 15:15 without a single day lost to shredded palms, something high-repetition sets promise. Switching hands every set to prevent skin loss is optimal for less-conditioned palms, and knocking out multiple sets with one arm before switching to another builds stellar strength endurance of the skin on the palms and the muscles of the hands, arms, shoulders, and upper back. Using sock sleeves or sweatbands while knocking out sets of 10 or more on each arm delivers indisputable gains to the student's grip while protecting the palms.

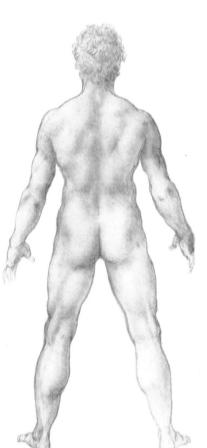

⊙ Doing the 15:15 protocol with a 16 kg kettlebell removed 5 pounds of body fat from my frame three months after I had lost 50 pounds following the Warrior Diet and basic RKC training. At an already lean body weight of 230 pounds after the tenth session of 15:15, I had lost nearly all fat from my midsection. In addition, my forearms had muscled up and their vascularity was unparalleled.

⊙ The training protocols, from cadence testing to lactate buffering, are concisely programmed and may allow the trainee to build his or her snatch IQ over the course of six to nine months, if the program is followed from its birth to its maturation. And when you have tested, timed, boosted, and buffered with one kettlebell, retest your cadence with a heavier-handled bell and follow the program again. You have the map: Now walk the line. ⚡

WILL WILLIAMS,
SENIOR RKC INSTRUCTOR
PHILADELPHIA, PA

Blood on My Hands, Blood on My Kettlebell

Last winter, Master RKC Mark Reifkind introduced me to Kenneth Jay's VO2max snatch protocol. Mark had been using the workout himself for a few months and extolled its virtues and challenges. When he proposed incorporating it into my training program, I confess to being as intimidated as I was intrigued—and I like a good arse kicking as much as any RKC "victim."

Mark, being the strategic, intelligent Master RKC that he is, plotted my progression into the protocol—waving the sets and reps to and fro, allowing me to develop the strength and endurance to set PRs on a regular basis with minimal discomfort and no injury. We focused on the 15:15 protocol and established my rep rate as seven or eight reps with the 12 kg and five or six with the 16 kg. We worked up the ladder of sets and reps a week at a time. For example, I did 35 sets of seven as a PR a couple of months into it, followed the next week by a combination of 20 sets of seven and 10 sets of eight, and so on, gradually and safely ratcheting up the load and the distance. Similarly, we waved the progression to the 16 kg, which is a heavy weight for me, although less so now that I've been pursing VO2max work. I'm hooked on it and have been since that first set so many months ago.

> I ripped my hands all to hell, but it was worth seeing blood on the kettlebell when I finished.

After learning more about Kenneth's work during the Level II RKC last summer, I was determined to hit the 80-set mark when I returned home. My previous highs were in the 40s and 50s, with some combination of seven and eight reps. While I still haven't achieved 80 sets of eight, I did hit 80 sets of seven with the 12 kg. I ripped my hands all to hell, but it was worth seeing blood on the kettlebell when I finished. It will take me a while to do the same with eight reps, but getting to 80 sets broke through a mental barrier that makes the next goal seem within reach. And at some point, I'll get to 80 sets of eight with the 16 kg. This goal is a stretch goal, but I believe the VO2max protocol facilitates achievement at a high level.

Not that any of this was easy! No, it's never been easy. I was right to be nervous in the beginning. The first time I tried the 15:15 protocol, the skimpy 15 or 20 sets of seven reps left me in a puddle of sweat, confusion, and exhilaration. I don't need to explain the sweating—it's hard the first time you do it. Actually, it's hard every time you do it (if you're doing it right, that is). The other feelings stemmed from an epiphany borne from extreme physical exertion. It was an almost spiritual "Eureka!" moment. I am new to strength training and even newer to kettlebells. I picked one up for the first time in January 2007 and fell in love enough to complete the Level I and II RKC. I've been a cyclist for a decade but never a competitive one.

This is all to say that I'm not experienced or smart enough to recognize training genius unless it's dropped on my head like a brick. And the simple elegance of Kenneth's VO2max protocol and its ability to engage a higher level of performance than I'd ever achieved was equal to genius being dropped on my head like a building's worth of bricks.

The workout tests your muscular strength, cardiovascular endurance, and mental focus with an advanced kettlebell snatch move that requires excellent form borne from a strong swing foundation—the cornerstone kettlebell movement that even the diehards dismiss at times. That's not allowed with this work, though. Measuring progress within the workout and over time requires only simple tools: an interval timer and maybe a heart rate monitor (if you don't want to count beats), plus a willingness do simple arithmetic.

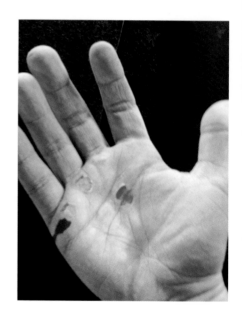

The cult of unquantifiable variety is blissfully unwelcome in the VO2max workout. You do so many sets of so many reps within 15 or 36 seconds or you don't, and this number is higher or lower than the last time you did it. You improve, you execute your training plan, or you don't. There's no hiding out!

VO2max has become integral to my training. In addition to being consistently fun and challenging, it uses time efficiently and covers all the bases as a stand-alone workout. These attributes alone recommend it.

However, I've experienced broader-reaching benefits from using this protocol. My overall physical preparedness for any athletic endeavor that interests me has been vastly improved. In the last year or two, kettlebells have dominated my workouts to the diminishment of road biking. However, I had no trouble participating in a 60-mile ride in a very hilly section of northern California after a winter that included no cycling but lots of VO2max. And now, I'm about to incorporate into my training regimen long (three-plus hour) hikes in challenging terrain, and it doesn't occur to me to ponder whether I need to work up to the distance.

I credit VO2max with offering both the athletic foundation and the mental discipline to try almost anything, even if activity-specific skill needs honing. Along the same lines, since emphasizing VO2max in my workout plans, I've remained more or less injury free and able to enjoy fairly rapid recovery from hard workouts.

If my words read like those of a zealot, that's because I am one. I'm a grateful and devout apostle of Kenneth's VO2max work. I honestly can't imagine how I'd ever have fun training without it.

Cindy Glass, RKC II
Portola Valley, CA

I Heart Max

My first rendezvous with Max, as I like to call this heart-throb of a workout, happened on February 17, 2008, on the final day of the RKC Certification course in San Jose, California. The original grad workout, which called for swings and see-saw presses, would have undoubtedly done a number on my shoulders, so I was ever so glad that Andrea Du Cane, Master RKC, in her infinite wisdom, proposed something else. And Max was *really* something else!

Of course, we didn't know we were doing the VO2max thing. There was no snatch cadence determination. We were simply told to snatch seven or eight reps for 15 seconds, rest, and then do it again with the other arm until *whenever*. Mark Reifkind, Master RKC, was in the middle of the field yelling out instructions, and apparently, he was to decide the "whenever" part. I came upon Max with trepidation and a certain eagerness. Our hands, properly "condomized" with tape or sock sleeves, were ready for the ritual slaughter.

Doing Max was truly exhilarating and unforgettable—high adrenaline, hot and sweaty, primal. Indelibly edged in my mind is this cacophony of sounds:

> *"Fast and loose! Fast and loose!" ROOOH AAAH!*
> *"Five, four, three, two, one snatch!" ROOOH AAAH!*
> *"Chalk? Chalk!" ROOOH AAAH!*
> *"Come on, Team Du Cane! Go, Team Du Pain!" ROOOH AAAH!*
> *"Go Team McCain!" Uh-oh.*

(I was in stitches when I heard that last one! Somebody was getting delirious.)

Then Pavel came around and told me to suck my left shoulder into the socket. I resolved not to look at my left hand. After all, a good vegan like me deserved better than the sight of shredded pork.

The mayhem that day lasted 25 minutes—50 rounds. No longer a VO2max virgin and wiser to the ways of cardiovascular conditioning, I can now look back at the grad workout and marvel at how far I've come in terms of strength and endurance.

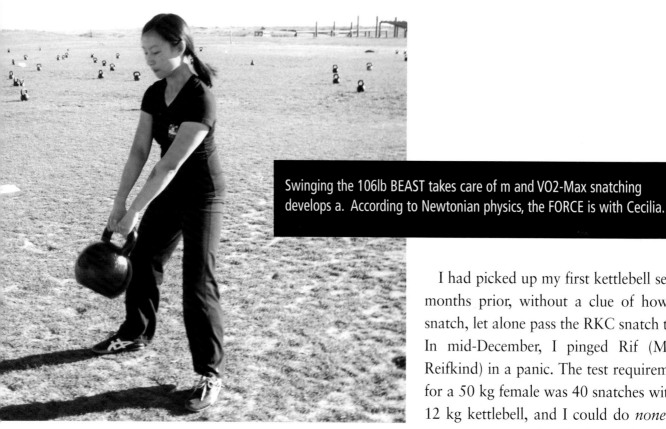

Swinging the 106lb BEAST takes care of m and VO2-Max snatching develops a. According to Newtonian physics, the FORCE is with Cecilia.

I had picked up my first kettlebell seven months prior, without a clue of how to snatch, let alone pass the RKC snatch test. In mid-December, I pinged Rif (Mark Reifkind) in a panic. The test requirement for a 50 kg female was 40 snatches with a 12 kg kettlebell, and I could do *none*. In the next two months, I had a grueling daily diet of heavy swings, snatches, and burpees, and I underwent involuntary cookie deprivation to make weight. I arrived in San Jose hungry, sleepy, and worried.

Day 1: Passed the snatch test. Did a million swings every time an airplane flew overhead. Felt great.

Day 2: Ate lots and lots of dessert at the banquet. Felt greater.

Day 3: Victimized two "guinea pigs" who came for the free lesson. Then did Max. Felt superlatively greatest.

When it was all over, I knew I could have done more—at least five more minutes. I didn't want it to be over. What Max showed me that day was that the RKC way of training—hard style!—had put me way ahead of the endurance curve, snatching as awkwardly as I did and being as neurologically retarded as I was (from my scoliosis).

Max charmingly presented itself to me as a test, not a protocol. And since I passed brilliantly (or so I thought), I relegated Max to the status of a one-night stand. I am not a competitive athlete and I don't play any sports, so what do I need Max for? Scrubbing floors? Ah, but wait!

Right around the time I started swinging kettlebells, I also joined a class called Cardio Taiko—a drum class with a workout focus. In the beginning, it was really just like a dance class with the added component of hitting drums with a stick. Gradually, our sensei shifted the emphasis to technique, rhythm, and conditioning.

The drills were killer for the shoulders. Imagine hitting a tennis ball forehand and backhand, respectively, with the right and left arm, continuously, furiously, relentlessly, in rounds that match the length and intensity of a typical MMA bout. Members of the taiko group Kodo are known for their legendary feat of running the entire Boston Marathon and then jumping on stage to perform at the finish line. Our sensei talks about them often. He wants us to have world-class stamina, world-class staying power.

So now, Max and I have regular dates. I have since learned that 80 is the new 50 and that 20 minutes of real work in 40 minutes of 15:15 snatching will confer Jedi powers to my cardiac muscles. To be honest, I dig Max. Snatching an 8 kg kettlebell is a piece of cake after the RKC snatch test. I recently restarted the protocol at 40 sets, 7 reps per set, and aim to add 8 sets per week until I hit 80.

I'm sure the piece of cake will soon begin to feel like a slosh pipe, but in the meantime, I am reveling in my cardio makeover. I am impatient during the breaks we take in taiko class. I just want to play for the full two hours. Max makes me want to play.

Because size matters! Left ventricle. Hard style!

Cecilia Tom, RKC,
San Francisco

Cecilia Tom, RKC, sucks O2 and emits CO2 in San Francisco. Her latest thought experiment, "Optimization of Collective VO2max Snatch Numbers via Carbon Emissions Trading," is based on the polluters-get-paid principle aimed to accelerate global warming. www.praxiskettlebell.com

Interview with Danish world-ranked Greco-Roman Wrestler Mark O. Madsen, RKC

BY KENNETH JAY

KJ: Mark, thanks for doing this interview. Can you start by telling a little bit about yourself?

Mark: Sure, my pleasure. My name is Mark Overgaard Madsen. I am 24 years old, and I wrestle on the Danish national team.

KJ: When did you start wrestling?

Mark: My grandfather introduced me to wrestling when I was 6 years old, and I immediately fell in love with the sport.

KJ: What are your best wrestling competition results?

Mark: I have two world silver medals and one world bronze medal. I have also beaten several of the best wrestlers in the world at other wrestling competitions and meets. I wrestle in –74 kg (–163 lbs).

KJ: Where can people see you wrestle on a daily basis?

Mark: My club is called BK Thor, and it's located in a town called Nykoebing in the southern part of Denmark. I also wrestle for a German club called Luckenwalde, and I compete every weekend in the German bundesliga—kicking ass!

KJ: Cool! Now to your physical training and preparation—and the kettlebell, in particular, which you are a big fan of. How did you find out about this round hunk of iron with a handle attached?

Mark: It was my strength and conditioning coach, Kenneth Jay, who introduced me to the kettlebell. I was hooked immediately and decided that I wanted to go through the RKC Instructor certification, which I did in May '07 in Denmark. The results I am getting from training with the kettlebell and being coached by Kenneth Jay are absolutely outstanding. It has no comparison.

KJ: Very good to hear! Now, how was it to go through the three grueling days of instructor training at the RKC? Can you tell us a little about that?

Mark: I had a great time. The in-depth knowledge of all the instructors was top notch, and it was great throwing kettlebells around for an entire weekend, learning all the subtleties of lifting correctly—subtleties that have improved my wrestling extensively. Kettlebell training is an awesome way to get in the best shape, in the most safe and effective way. I train with kettlebells every day, and I wouldn't miss it for the world.

KJ: That is awesome! What are some of your favorite lifts and exercises?

Mark: The number 1 of the ballistic lifts is definitely the snatch, because of the perfect combination of explosive movement and cardiovascular conditioning. It has no equal. Other than that, I really like the two-hands anyhow in a slightly modified version my coach instructed me in doing, and the get-up is also a stable part of my training regime. A lot of the RKC lifts and exercises fit perfectly with my wrestling. . . . The Viking Push Press has also for a long time been a favorite of mine. If I have to choose one lift only, then it's got to be the snatch.

KJ: Is the kettlebell the only tool you use in your training?

Mark: No, far from it. I use a variety of tools. My training is designed around the basics like the deadlift, military press, bench press, pull-up, the Olympic lifts and their variations, along with more specific stuff that my coach has designed. I also do a lot of grip training. Depending on the annual training plan and when it is competition preparation, my coach puts together the program. I am always lifting kettlebells, but depending on where the focus is, I am doing it accordingly. Coming closer to competitions, the kettlebell is probably the main tool, because it is so easy to tax my stamina and I always breathe hard.

KJ: You have been doing the 15:15 MVO2 protocol ever since it was designed. What do you think about it?

Mark: It is gruelingly tough. In relation to what I do on the mat, it is the best preparation I have ever done. It really works like you wouldn't believe.

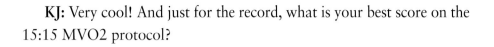

KJ: Very cool! And just for the record, what is your best score on the 15:15 MVO2 protocol?

Mark: I consistently hit 80 sets doing 8 reps per 15 seconds with a 24 kg kettlebell.

KJ: That is amazing! How much do you weigh?

Mark: 80 kg (176 lbs.).

KJ: Wow, that is a huge workload! Not many people are able to do that. What is next for Mark O. Madsen?

Mark: Well, I will continue to improve my wrestling and my strength and conditioning and get more metal at international competitions. The next big competition is the world championships held here in Denmark, Herning, September 2009.

KJ: Sounds good. Now that you are an RKC, is there any chance that the attendees at the Danish RKC next year in May will see you there as an assistant instructor?

Mark: That is very possible!

KJ: Mark, thank you so much for taking the time to have this little talk.

Currently, Mark is ranked 2nd in the world by http://www.themat.com.

9

Call to
Action

iking warriors of the world unite! I propose a call to action to reclaim the glory of our heroic forefathers. Reclaim the level of physical performance that was once ours, and start building a heart of elastic steel with explosive power that never quits!

I cannot promise you that it will be easy.

I cannot promise you that it will be over quickly.

And I cannot promise you that you will enjoy it.

I can promise you, though, a transformation of your body unlike no other, if you have the courage to stay with the Viking Warrior Conditioning regime. Whether your battle takes place in the ring, on the mat, on the court, on the streets, in a house, or at sea, you will stand tall, knowing your physical performance level will surpass that of anyone or anything that comes your way. A true Viking Warrior comes prepared, never backs down, and fights for victory in any endeavor!

In the glory days of the Battle of Valhalla, not having enough power–endurance meant certain death. Being strong is great, but without power–endurance, it doesn't mean anything in life.

Build power–endurance the Viking Warrior way, and you will prevail!

Appendix:
Viking Warrior Snatch Mastery 101

The Viking Warrior Conditioning regime requires you to be very proficient in the Tsar of kettlebell lifts—the Snatch. If your technique is suspect, I encourage you to seek out an RKC instructor in your area (there is a complete list of RKC instructors at www.dragondoor.com). Have them check out your form and make the necessary corrections before taking on the Viking Warrior Conditioning regime.

To provide you with a little extra help on dialing in your snatch form here is a step-by-step protocol for ultimate snatch mastery—like a Viking!

The snatch is very much like a three stage rocket. The fist stage is the powerful thrust of the hip extensors to get the kettlebell going. As with a rocket launch, this action is the explosion that generates enough thrust to get liftoff. The second stage is the upper body pull. The upper body pull provides additional acceleration to the kettlebell while taming the arc. In the rocket analogy this compares to the first afterburner firing when the empty fuel tanks have been dumped off the rocket. The rocket continues to accelerate and so does the kettlebell. The third stage of the kettlebell snatch is the punch-through. The forces added to this final stage are low but the velocity is very high. The kettlebell rotates around and you catch it in the lockout—the "Viking Victory pose". To use the rocket analogy again, the final afterburner fires and shuts off when the rocket is out of the atmosphere.

How to do it!

Step 1:
Revisit the swing. The swing is the foundation of the snatch. If you can't swing then you definitely can't snatch.

Start with the kettlebell in front of you on the ground. Push your hips back, keeping a neutral spine and grab the kettlebell in the center of the handle. Pull it back between your legs and immediately reverse the movement by forcefully extending the hips and knees at the same time. It should be a swift hip-snap. Do not try to muscle it with the arm but rather rely on the powerful hip extension to get the kettlebell going. Make sure that your lat is tight and the arm is not disconnected from the torso.

For a further breakdown of the swing please revisit *Enter the Kettlebell!* book and DVD by Pavel Tsatsouline. Both are available at www.dragondoor.com.

Step 2:

When the kettlebell is moving pull it closer to your body using your upper back while bending your elbow slightly. The motion is comparable to starting a lawnmover and it will tame the arc of the kettlebell making it move faster.

Step 3:

This is the swift catch of the kettlebell as it rotates around your hand. Actively go around the kettlebell with the hand as opposed to letting the kettlebell rotate and hit you on the forearm. You should be meeting the kettlebell making the catch smooth and subtle. You will end up in the lockout—the Viking Victory pose!

Step 4:

The kettlebell has to come down and the way to do it correctly is to reverse the action. The bell rotates first. The Viking Warrior snatch calls for going over the top instead of around the wrist. The kettlebell is not that heavy and we want maximum force generation; thus we need to accelerate it as much as possible and going around the wrist will negate that.

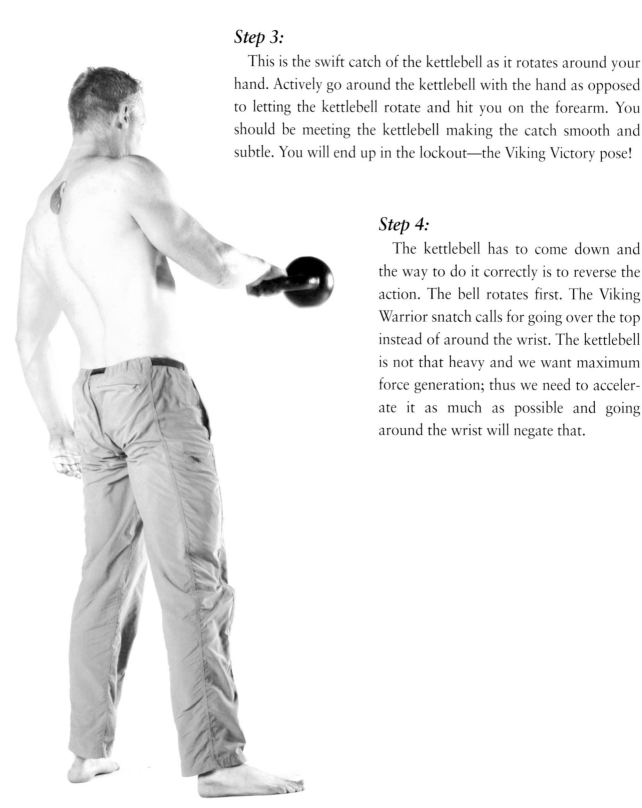

Step 5:

Again tame the arc after the rotation of the kettlebell. The latissimus dorsi (the big upper body pulling muscle) should contract forcefully adding acceleration to the kettlebell beyond the gravitational pull. The kettlebell is not just falling but is being pulled down faster that gravity naturally allows. PLEASE NOTE: The hips have not moved yet! I repeat: The hips have NOT moved yet.

Step 6:

This is the hike pass of the kettlebell. Imagine tossing it through your stomach and quickly and explosively getting out of the way. This is accomplished by moving the hips back and is the crucial part of maximum power generation. The hips are not just pushed back but punched back. The distinction between the two is all-important! Imagine that you are punching with your butt. The movement of the hips should be comparable to a punch. A punch is faster and more powerful than a push and a Viking likes more power! Kettlebells Los Angeles' chief instructor Dr. Mark Cheng made me aware of this important distinction while teaching Guru Inosanto at the Inosanto Academy during my first visit in LA back in August 08. "Doc" has a great way of teaching it. Stand with your back to a heavy bag and simply punch it with your butt. The cueing is that you want to make a dent in the heavybag instead of just pushing it away. A partner observing you doing this is a great help.

Catching the kettlebell coming back between your legs with a butt-punch creates a greater stretch reflex response of your hip extensors thus generating more force when going into the next repetition. This is the essence of Overspeed Eccentrics!

Now go berserk and be a VIKING!

GLOSSARY OF CARDIOVASCULAR PHYSIOLOGY

Afterload. Refers to the resistance the heart must overcome when ejecting blood.

A-V O2 difference. The difference in oxygen content between the blood in the arteries and the venoules.

Baroreceptors. Receptors that register blood pressure changes.

CO. Cardiac output. CO = HR x SV.

Compliance. How easily something is stretched.

Concentric hypertrophy. Refers to the thickening of the heart wall.

Eccentric hypertrophy. Refers to the expansion of the heart chambers.

EDV. End diastolic volume. The volume of blood in the left ventricle of the heart at the end of the filling phase (relaxation phase) of the heartbeat cycle.

Ejection fraction. The fraction of blood ejected from the heart with every heartbeat. The left ventricle will not empty completely during ejection. The ejection fraction equals the ejected blood divided by the total blood volume of the left ventricle.

ESV. End systolic volume. The volume of blood in the left ventricle of the heart at the end of the ejection phase (contraction phase) of the heartbeat cycle.

HR. Heart rate.

Inotrophy. Refers to the strength of the heart muscle.

Preload. Refers to the filling of the heart ventricles.

SV. Stroke volume. The amount of blood ejected from the left ventricle of the heart with every heartbeat. SV = EDV – ESV.

Valsalva maneuver. Exhaling forcefully through a closed or almost closed glottis.

VO2. The amount of oxygen uptake on a whole-body level. VO2 = CO x A-V O2 difference.

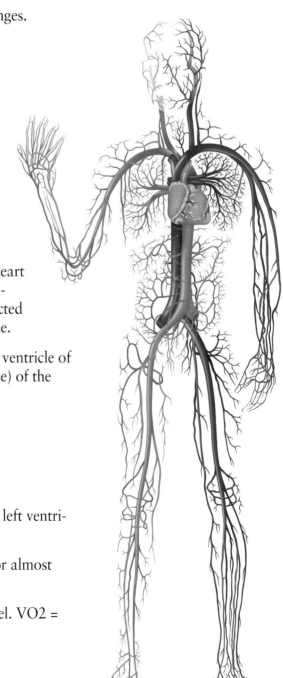

CONSULTED WORKS

Aagaard P., Simonsen E.B., Andersen J.L., Magnusson S.P., Halkjaer-Kristensen J., & Dyhre-Poulsen P. (2000). Neural inhibition during maximal eccentric and concentric quadriceps contraction: Effects of resistance training. *Journal of Applied Physiology*, 89(6): 2249–2257.

American College of Sports Medicine. (2000). *ACSM's Advanced Exercise Physiology*. Philadelphia: Lippincott Williams & Wilkins.

Åstrand P. O., & Rodahl K. (1986). *Textbook of Work Physiology*. New York: McGraw-Hill.

Baechle T.R., & Earle R.W. (2000). *Essentials of Strength Training and Conditioning* (2nd ed.). Champaign, IL: Human Kinetics.

Beckham S.G., & Earnest C.P. (2000, June). Metabolic cost of free weight circuit weight training. *Journal of Sports Medicine and Physical Fitness*, 40(2): 118–125.

Berry M., & Moritani T. (1985). The effects of various training intensities on the kinetics of oxygen consumption. *Journal of Sports Medicine*, 25, 77–83.

Boron W.F., & Boulpaep E.L. (2005). *Medical Physiology* (rev. ed.). Philadelphia: Elsevier Saunders.

Carter S.L., Rennie C.D., Hamilton S.J., & Tarnopolsky M.A. (2001). Changes in skeletal muscle in males and females following endurance training. *Canadian Journal of Physiology and Pharmacology*, 79, 386–392.

Casaburi R., Storer T.W., Ben-Dov I., & Wasserman K. (1987). Effect of endurance training on possible determinants of VO2 during heavy exercise. *Journal of Applied Physiology*, 62(1): 199–207.

Casaburi R., Storer T.W., Ben-Dov I., & Wasserman K. (1995). Evaluation of blood lactate elevations as an intensity criterion for exercise training. *Medicine and Science in Sports and Exercise*, 27(6): 852–862.

Davis J., Frank M.H., Whipp B.J., & Wassermann K. (1979). Anaerobic threshold alterations caused by endurance training in middle-aged men. *Journal of Applied Physiology*, 46,1039–1046.

Dempsey J.A., Vidruk E.H., & Mitchell G.S. (1985). Pulmonary control systems in exercise: Update. *Fed Proc*, 44, 2260–2270.

Dintiman G.B., & Ward R.D. (2003). *Sports Speed* (3rd ed.). Champaign, IL: Human Kinetics.

Enoka R.M. (2001). *Neuromechanics of Human Movement* (3rd ed.). Champaign, IL: Human Kinetics.

Frayn K.N. (1997). *Metabolic Regulation* (2nd ed.). New York: Blackwell.

Gaesser G.A., Ward S.A., Baum V.C., & Whipp B.J. (1992). Effects of infused epinephrine on slow phase of O2 uptake kinetics during heavy exercise in humans. *Journal of Applied Physiology*, 77(5): 2413–2419.

Gaesser G.A. (1994). Influence of endurance training and catecholamines on exercise VO2 response. *Medicine and Science in Sports and Exercise*, 26(11): 1342–1346.

Gettman L.R., & Pollock M.L. (1981). Circuit weight training: a critical review of its physiological benefits. *Physician and Sports Medicine*, 9, 44–60.

Gotshalk L.A., Berger R.A., & Kraemer W.J. (2004). Cardiovascular responses to a high-volume continuous circuit resistance training protocol. *Journal of Strength and Conditioning Research*, 18(4): 760–764.

Grassi, B. (2001). Regulation of oxygen consumption at the onset of exercise: Is it really controversial? *Exercise and Sport Sciences Reviews*, 29, 134–138.

Hagberg J.M., Hickson R.C., Ehsani A.A., & Hollozy J.O. (1980). Faster adjustments to and from recovery from submaximal exercise in the trained state. *Journal of Applied Physiology*, 48, 218–224.

Hagberg J.M., Mullin J.P., & Nagle F.J. (1978). Oxygen consumption during constant-load exercise. *Journal of Applied Physiology*, 45(3): 381–384.

Haltom R.W., Kraemer R.R., Sloan R.A., Hebert E.P., Frank K., & Tryniecki J.L. (1999, November). Circuit weight training and its effects on excess postexercise oxygen consumption. *Medicine and Science in Sports Exercise*, 31(11): 1613–1618.

Hatfield F.C. (1989). *Power— A Scientific Approach*. New York: McGraw-Hill.

Hawley J. (2002). Adaptations of skeletal muscle to prolonged, intense endurance training, *Clinical and Experimental Pharmacology and Physiology*, 29, 218–222.

Hickson R., Bomze H., & Holloszy J.O. (1977). Linear increase in aerobic power induced by a strenuous program of endurance exercise. *Journal of Applied Physiology*, 42(3): 372–376.

Hughson R.L., Tschakovsky M.E., & Houston M.E. (2001). Regulation of oxygen consumption at the onset of exercise. *Exercise and Sport Sciences Reviews*, 29, 129–133.

Klabunde R.E. (2005). *Cardiovascular Physiology Concepts*. Philadelphia: Lippincott Williams & Wilkins.

Kraemer W.J., & Häkkinen K. (2002). *Strength Training for Sport*. New York: Blackwell.

Kreider R.B., Fry A.C., & O'Toole M.L. (1998). *Overtraining in Sport*. Champaign, IL: Human Kinetics.

Kreighbaum E., & Barthels K.M. (1986). *Biomechanics— A Qualitative Approach for Studying Human Movement* (4th ed.). Boston: Allyn & Bacon.

Krustrup P.R. (2004). *Muscle Oxygen Uptake and Energy Turnover during Dynamic Exercise in Humans*. Doctoral thesis, Institute of Exercise and Sports Sciences, University of Copenhagen, Denmark.

Kushmerick M.J., Meyer R.A., & Brown T.R. (1992). Regulation of oxygen consumption in fast- and slow-twitch muscle. *American Journal of Physiology–Cell Physiology*, 263, C598–C606.

LeMura L.M., & von Duvillard S.P. (2004). *Clinical Exercise Physiology*. Philadelphia: Lippincott Williams & Wilkins.

Little J. (1998). *The Art of Expressing the Human Body*. North Clarendon, VT: Tuttle.

Mazetti S., Douglass M., Yocum A., & Harber M. (2007, August). Effect of explosive versus slow contractions and exercise intensity on energy expenditure. *Medicine and Science in Sports and Exercise*, 39(8): 1291–1301.

McArdle W.D., Katch F.I., & Katch V.L. (2001). *Exercise Physiology—Energy, Nutrition and Human Performance* (5th ed.). Philadelphia: Lippincott Williams & Wilkins.

McArdle W.D., Katch F.I., & Katch V.L. (2006). *Essentials of Exercise Physiology* (3rd ed.). Philadelphia: Lippincott Williams & Wilkins.

Michalsik L., & Bangsbo J. (2002). *Aerob og Anaerob træning*. Brondby, Denmark: Danmarks Idræts-Forbund.

Millet G.P., Jaouen B., Borrani F., & Candau R. (2002, August). Effects of concurrent endurance and strength training on running economy and VO(2) kinetics. *Medicine and Science in Sports and Exercise*, 34(8): 1351–1359.

Moritani T., & deVries H.A. (1979, June). Neural factors versus hypertrophy in the time course of muscle strength gain. *American Journal of Physical Medicine and Rehabilitation*, 58(3): 115–130.

Murray, A., Delaney T., & Bell C. (2006, March). Rapid onset and offset of circulatory adaptations to exercise training in men. *Journal of Human Hypertension*, 20(3): 193–200.

Nagle F., & Irmin L. (1960). Effects on two systems of weight training on circulation, respiration, endurance and related physiological factors. *Research Quarterly*, 31, 607–615.

Roston W.L., Whipp B.J., Davis J.A., Cunningham D.A., Effros R.M., & Wasserman K. (1987). Oxygen uptake kinetics and lactate concentration during exercise in humans. *American Review of Respiratory Diseases*, 135, 1080–1084.

Sahlin K., Harris R.C., & Hultman E. (1975, November). Creatine kinase equilibrium and lactate content compared with muscle pH in tissue samples obtained after isometric exercise. *Biochemistry Journal*, 152(2): 173–180.

Saltin B., Blomqvist G., & Mitchell J.H. (1968). Response to exercise after bed rest and after training: A longitudinal study of adaptive changes in oxygen transport and body composition. *Circulation*, 38(Suppl VII): 1–78.

Saltin B., Rådegran G., Koskolu M.D., & Roach R.C. (1998). Skeletal muscle blood flow in humans and its regulation during exercise. *Acta Physiologica Scandinavica*, 162, 421.

Schaible T.F., & Scheuer J. (1985). Cardiac adaptations to chronic exercise. *Progress in Cardiovascular Diseases*, 27, 297–324.

Scheuer J., & Tipton C.M. (1977). Cardiovacular adaptations to physical training. *Annual Review of Physiology*, 39, 221–251.

Shinohara M., & Moritani T. (1992). Increase in neuromuscular activity and oxygen uptake during heavy exercise. *Annals of Physiological Anthropology*, 11(3): 257–262.

Tsatsouline P. (2006). *Enter the Kettlebell*. St. Paul, MN: Dragon Door.

Van Cutsem M., Duchateau J., & Hainaut K. (1998, November 15). Changes in single motor unit behaviour contribute to the increase in contraction speed after dynamic training in humans. *Journal of Physiology*, 513(Part 1): 295–305.

Voropayev V.I. (1984). Kettle-bell lifting as an effective mean of physical education. *Weightlifting Yearbook 1984*. Moscow: Fizkultura i Sport.

West J.B. (2005). *Respiratory Physiology—The Essentials* (7th ed.). Philadelphia: Lippincott Williams & Wilkins.

Whipp B.J. (1987). *Dynamics of pulmonary gas exchange*. Circulation, 76, V118–V128.

Willis W.T., & Jackman M.R. (1994). Mitochondrial function during heavy exercise. *Medicine and Science in Sports and Exercise*, 26(11): 1347–1353.

Yessis M. (1988). *Secrets of Soviet Sports Fitness and Training*. New York: William Morrow.

Zatsiorsky V.M. (1995). *Science and Practice of Strength Training*. Champaign, IL: Human Kinetics.

İ П D E X

ABOUT THE AUTHOR

Kenneth Jay, (b. 1978), holds a University Degree in Exercise Physiology from the University of Copenhagen, August Krogh Institute. Kenneth was the first in the Western world to conduct a university-level study on the cardiovascular benefits of high-repetition kettlebell snatches.

Based in a small town not far from Copenhagen, Kenneth coaches the Danish Olympic athletes, including several world gold, silver, and bronze medalists in Greco-Roman wrestling and swimming. Kenneth also teaches on a regular basis at Dragon Door's RKC Certifications in the United States and other countries. In addition, Kenneth is a sought-after lecturer on strength and conditioning, and he has conducted several seminars for elite Danish military and police units, among others. Kenneth also hosts the Danish RKC Certification and runs his own company, Kettlebells.Dk.

Kenneth is the author of the acclaimed DVD *Advanced Strength Strategies—Cardiovascular Kettlebell Concepts*, which is an in-depth lecture on cardiovascular physiology applied to kettlebell training. The DVD is available online at www.DragonDoor.com.

In his spare time, Kenneth practices what he preaches and aspires to compete in wrestling, boxing, and arm wrestling. He also practices the martial art of Jeet Kune Do (JKD).

THE DANE OF PAIN COMMANDS YOU TO FINALLY GET REAL:

ENOUGH IS ENOUGH!

End the *indignity and shame* of modern-day *softness*—using this ultimate protocol for building a **JACK-HAMMER HEART** and the **INVINCIBLE HARDINESS** of an ancient warrior

With pointers, charts, diagrams, stats and wads of research to back him up, Kenneth Jay delivers convincing proof that a **carefully calculated, personalized kettlebell snatch protocol can** give us the most outstanding cardio of our lives. And give us a fighting chance to be mentioned in the same breath as those immensely powerful warriors of ancient times.

The Level II RKCs got a thorough schooling in *Cardiovascular Kettlebell Concepts* and how to massively enhance their all-important **VO2Max.**

But theory without practice is like decaf coffee—why bother?

Well, of course our kind Viking was not about to let his students off with a mere Powerpoint presentation of theory and research, however convincing. So, out to the playing field the RKCs all trooped—and were promptly subjected to one of the most blistering KB sessions of their lives: the **VO2Max snatch protocol.**

Again, we caught it all on tape: every detail of Kenneth's superb and highly educational presentation and every important moment of the VO2Max protocol in action.

Absorb Kenneth's presentation, watch it through a few times so your mind can understand the full significance and power of what Kenneth is offering you. Follow along and "take heart" from the warrior-building workout that follows. Then prepare to kick some solid butt in the world at large.

2 Mid-Level **3** Advanced

2-DVD set
#DV049 *$77.00*

Advanced Strength Strategies
An Advanced RKC Training Resource
With Kenneth Jay
Running Time:
One hour 42 minutes

THE WORLD'S #1 HANDHELD GYM FOR EXTREME FITNESS

Use Kettlebells to:

- **Accelerate your all-purpose strength**—so you can readily handle the toughest demands
- **Hack away your fat**—without the dishonor of dieting and aerobics
- **Boost your physical resilience**—to repel the hardest hits
- **Build your staying power**—to endure and conquer, whatever the distance
- **Create a potent mix of strength-with-flexibility**—to always reach your target
- **Forge a fighter's physique**—so form matches function
- **Be independent**—world's #1 portable gym makes you as strong as you want to be, anywhere, anytime

Kettlebells Fly Air Force One!

"There's a competitive reason behind the appearance of kettlebells at the back doors and tent flaps of military personnel. When Russian and US Special Forces started competing against each other after the Soviet Union broke up, the Americans made a disturbing discovery. "We'd be totally exhausted and the Russians wouldn't even be catching their breath," says... [a] Secret Service agent... "It turned out they were all working with kettlebells."

Now, half the Secret Service is snatching kettlebells and a set sometimes travels with the President's detail on Air Force One."—*Christian Science Monitor*

Pavel's Kettlebell FAQ

What is a 'kettlebell'?

A 'kettlebell' or girya (Russ.) is a traditional Russian cast iron weight that looks like a cannonball with a handle. The ultimate tool for extreme all-round fitness.

The kettlebell goes way back – it first appeared in a Russian dictionary in 1704 (Cherkikh, 1994). So popular were kettlebells in Tsarist Russia that any strongman or weightlifter was referred to as a girevik, or 'a kettlebell man'.

"Not a single sport develops our muscular strength and bodies as well as kettlebell athletics," reported Russian magazine Hercules in 1913.

"Kettlebells—Hot Weight of the Year"—Rolling Stone

Why train with kettlebells?

Because they deliver extreme all-round fitness. And no single other tool does it better. Here is a short list of hardware the Russian kettlebell replaces: barbells, dumbbells, belts for weighted pullups and dips, thick bars, lever bars, medicine balls, grip devices, and cardio equipment.

Vinogradov & Lukyanov (1986) found a very high correlation between the results posted in a kettlebell lifting competition and a great range of dissimilar tests: strength, measured with the three powerlifts and grip strength; strength endurance, measured with pullups and parallel bar dips; general endurance, determined by a 1000 meter run; work capacity and balance, measured with special tests.

Voropayev (1983) tested two groups of subjects in pullups, a standing broad jump, a 100m sprint, and a 1k run. He put the control group on a program that emphasized the above tests; the experimental group lifted kettlebells. In spite of the lack of practice on the tested exercises, the kettlebell group scored better in every one of them! This is what we call "the what the hell effect".

Kettlebells melt fat without the dishonor of dieting or aerobics. If you are overweight, you will lean out. If you are skinny, you will get built up. According to Voropayev (1997) who studied top Russian gireviks, 21.2% increased their bodyweight since taking up kettlebelling and 21.2% (the exact same percentage, not a typo), mostly heavyweights, decreased it. The Russian kettlebell is a powerful tool for fixing your body comp, whichever way it needs fixing.

Kettlebells forge doers' physiques along the lines of antique statues: broad shoulders with just a hint of pecs, back muscles standing out in bold relief, wiry arms, rugged forearms, a cut-up midsection, and strong legs without a hint of squatter's chafing.

Liberating and aggressive as medieval swordplay, kettlebell training is highly addictive. What other piece of exercise equipment can boast that its owners name it? Paint it? Get tattoos of it? Our Russian kettlebell is the Harley-Davidson of strength hardware.

"Kettlebells—A Workout with Balls"—Men's Journal

Who trains with kettlebells?

Hard comrades of all persuasions.

Soviet weightlifting legends such as Vlasov, Zhabotinskiy, and Alexeyev started their Olympic careers with old-fashioned kettlebells. Yuri Vlasov once interrupted an interview he was giving to a Western journalist and proceeded to press a pair of kettlebells. "A wonderful exercise," commented the world champion. "...It is hard to find an exercise better suited for developing strength and flexibility simultaneously."

The Russian Special Forces personnel owe much of their wiry strength, explosive agility, and never-quitting stamina to kettlebells. *Soldier, Be Strong!*, the official Soviet armed forces strength training manual pronounced kettlebell drills to be "one of the most effective means of strength development" representing "a new era in the development of human strength-potential".

The elite of the US military and law enforcement instantly recognized the power of the Russian kettlebell, ruggedly simple and deadly effective as an AK-47. You can find Pavel's certified RKC instructors among Force Recon Marines, Department of Energy nuclear security teams, the FBI's Hostage Rescue Team, the Secret Service Counter Assault Team, etc.

Once the Russian kettlebell became a hit among those whose life depends on their strength and conditioning, it took off among hard people from all walks of life: martial artists, athletes, regular hard comrades.

"I can't think of a more practical way of special operations training... I was extremely skeptical about kettlebell training and now wish that I had known about it fifteen years ago..."

—*Name withheld, Special Agent, U.S. Secret Service Counter Assault Team*

Am I kettlebell material?

Kettlebell training is extreme but not elitist. At the 1995 Russian Championship the youngest contestant was 16, the oldest 53! And we are talking elite competition here; the range is even wider if you are training for yourself rather than for the gold. Dr. Krayevskiy, the father of the kettlebell sport, took up training at the age of forty-one and twenty years later he was said to look fresher and healthier than at forty.

Only 8.8% of top Russian *gireviks*, members of the Russian National Team and regional teams, reported injuries in training or competition (Voropayev, 1997). A remarkably low number, especially if you consider that these are elite athletes who push their bodies over the edge. Many hard men with high mileage have overcome debilitating injuries with kettlebell training (get your doctor's approval). Acrobat Valentin Dikul fell and broke his back at seventeen. Today, in his mid-sixties, he juggles 180-pound balls and breaks powerlifting records!

"... kettlebells are a unique conditioning tool and a powerful one as well that you should add to your arsenal of strength... my experience with them has been part of what's led me to a modification in my thoughts on strength and bodyweight exercises... I'm having a blast training with them and I think you will as well."

—Bud Jeffries, the author of *How to Squat 900lbs. without Drugs, Powersuits, or Kneewraps*

How do I learn to use the kettlebell?

From Pavel's books and videos: *The Russian Kettlebell Challenge* or *From Russia with Tough Love* for comrades ladies. From an RKC certified instructor; find one in your area on RussianKettlebell.com. Kettlebell technique can be learned in one or two sessions and you can start intense training during the second or even first week (Dvorkin, 2001).

"...I felt rejuvenated and ready to conquer the world. I was sold on the kettlebells, as the exercises were fun and challenging, and demanded coordination, explosion, balance, and power... I am now on my way to being a better, fitter, and more explosive grappler, and doing things I haven't done in years!"

—Kid Peligro, *Grappling* magazine

What is the right kettlebell size for me?

Kettlebells come in 'poods'. A pood is an old Russian measure of weight, which equals 16kg, or roughly 35 lbs. An average man should start with a 35-pounder. It does not sound like a lot but believe it; it feels a lot heavier than it should! Most men will eventually progress to a 53-pounder, the standard issue size in the Russian military. Although available in most units, 70-pounders are used only by a few advanced guys and in elite competitions. 88-pounders are for mutants.

An average woman should start with an 18-pounder. A strong woman can go for a 26-pounder. Some women will advance to a 35-pounder. A few hard women will go beyond.

"Kettlebells are like weightlifting times ten."

"Kettlebells are like weightlifting times ten. ...If I could've met Pavel in the early '80s, I might've won two gold medals. I'm serious."

—Dennis Koslowski, D.C., RKC,
Olympic Silver Medalist in Greco-Roman Wrestling

CLASSIC KETTLEBELLS (SOLID CAST IRON/POWDER COATING)

Item	Weight in pounds	Price	MAIN USA	AK&HI	CAN
#P10N	10	$47.00	S/H $13.50	$55.50	$36.00
#P10P	14	$55.00	S/H $16.50	$66.50	$38.00
#P10M	18	$63.00	S/H $20.50	$73.50	$46.00
#P10G	26	$73.00	S/H $28.50	$88.50	$56.00
#P10A	35	$79.95	S/H $33.50	$104.50	$68.00
#P10H	44	$87.95	S/H $40.50	$122.50	$80.00
#P10B	53	$96.95	S/H $44.50	$139.50	$92.00
#P10J	62	$114.95	S/H $47.50	$157.50	$101.00
#P10C	70	$123.95	S/H $48.50	$175.50	$111.00
#P10Q	79	$140.95	S/H $53.50	$193.50	$125.00
#P10F	88	$158.95	S/H $58.50	$211.50	$138.00
#P10R	97	$199.95	S/H $64.50	$229.50	$153.00
#P10L	106	$218.95	S/H $69.50	$247.50	$167.00

SAVE! ORDER A SET OF CLASSIC KETTLEBELLS & SAVE $$$

#SP10	Classic Set—35, 53 & 70 lb.	Save $15.00	$285.95	S/H $126.50	$419.50	$271.00
#SP11	Women's Set—10, 14 & 18 lb.	Save $10.00	$149.95	S/H $50.50	$195.50	$120.00

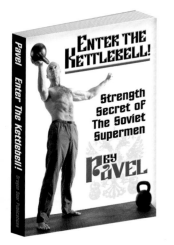

ENTER THE KETTLEBELL!

Strength Secret of The Soviet Supermen

By PAVEL

"Pavel's *Enter the Kettlebell!* helps you weed out weakness... develop explosive power, strength and never-quit endurance—with his PROVEN system for rapid, spectacular and across-the-board gains in physical performance"

The kettlebell has proved its worth many times over since Pavel has introduced it to America. Elite athletes, fighters, special operators, and regular hard Comrades swear by the extraordinary strength and conditioning delivered by this ancient Russian tool. Now, it is YOUR turn to *Enter the Kettlebell!*

For a kettlebell novice, the hardest part is knowing where to begin. And what you really need to do to get off to a **quick—yet rock-solid—start.** Pavel delivers.

For the Comrade who's already put in a year or two of kettlebell time, it's easy to hit a plateau after explosive early gains. Pavel knocks him out of his sophomore slump and helps him take his game to a higher level.

Then there's the grizzled KB vet who's been around the block and got too arrogant to practice his fundamentals (or never learned them in the first place). Pavel **hammers the fundamentals** because "it is the mastery of the basics that separates the elite from the rest."

With *Enter the Kettlebell!* Pavel has done all the work for you— honing a masterplan of essential training secrets that guarantee to make you powerful, resilient, and enduring—if you simply follow the proven guidelines.

Lift Your Kettlebell Like a Pro...

- **Are you** making these beginner's mistakes in your training?
- **Nine secrets** of greater strength and reduced injuries
- **Get the most** technique improvement with the least instruction
- How to **stop** fighting your body and get stronger
- **These two** movements will give you the biggest bang for your KB buck
- **Discover** a "simple & sinister" routine for killer conditioning and muscular shoulders
- **A common cause** of back pain after workouts—you would never guess what it is!—and how to avoid it
- How to **stretch your back** after training—everyone does it wrong
- **One style** of breathing will weaken you and make your back vulnerable—the other style of breathing gives you the explosive power of a trained fighter... know which is which

- The top five reasons RKC kettlebell training is great for your back
- **You have been misled:** sucking your stomach in does not protect your back but makes it more vulnerable! How to really protect your back when lifting
- **Reducing the odds** of arthritis—with ballistic loading
- **A surefire shortcut** to loosening stuck shoulders
- How to temper your shoulders for sports that trash them
- **A great visualization** for resilient elbows and shoulders
- **Why** cool-downs are important to your heart health
- **What you must know** about your heart rate and kettlebell training

- **The new prescription** for a power pump heart and great body composition
- **This little-known drill guarantees** improvement in your squatting depth, flexibility, technique and power

- **How to** make a simple towel your kettlebell coach— and reach your training goals faster
- **Get this one** foundational drill down—and most of the remaining exercises will be a piece of cake to learn and master
- **Why** most Comrades should choose pulls over squats
- **How to strengthen** your legs and hips without blowing them up

- **How to time** the hip movement for maximum explosive power
- **How to be** the indisputable master of the force you generate
- **Understand** the crucial value of "slow strength" training—the counterintuitive and rarely revealed secret of Russian athletic might
- **What it takes** to be more resilient in the ring
- **A simple way** to increase an experienced fighter's punching power
- **How to master** the natural athletic rhythm of tension and relaxation
- **A killer one-two combination** for the gym and ring
- **The key characteristics** of a kettlebell pro's press
- **Master this skill** and you will wield awesome pressing power
- **How to** make the heaviest kettlebell feel like a toy in your hand
- **Prof. Verkhoshansky's secret** for improving your strength by up to twenty percent
- **How** amateurs "leak" strength from their knees—and how pros fix the drain
- **How to get the most** out of your press while putting the least amount of stress on your shoulders
- **A unique** isometric drill to improve your pressing power
- **Where to look**—and not look—when pressing

- **An unexpected** assistance exercise for achieving a one-arm pull up
- **Smoke** your abs and obliques the old fashioned way
- A foolproof method for accelerating the curve on snatch mastery

- **The snatch** is a three-stage rocket—how to finesse the stages
- **How to avoid** bruising the forearm when snatching
- **A crucial warning about** shoulders and elbows in your first year of snatches
- **How to accomplish** the USSS Counter Assault Team 10-min snatch test—and be a man among men
- **How to keep** your training targeted while still having fun with new exercises
- **How to idiot-proof** your kettlebell workout—for consistently powerful gains

- **The little-understood but crucial** value of "in-between-strength"
- **Russian research** finds the day of the week when you are strongest—and it is not Monday
- **Work harder?** Or do more work?
- **The "ladder" method** for highly effective strength building

- **The kettlebell rules** for conditioning
- **A gambler's method** for deciding your high-rep workout
- **How to** log your workouts for optimal results
- **How to use** timed sets—for a foolproof and flexible practice

- **What** makes the kettlebell superior to other weights and fitness equipment?
- **Should you** train with the kettlebell as a stand-alone tool or mix it up with a barbell and dumbbells?
- **How to get superior** gains in athletic performance without sport specific training
- **The kettlebell "what the hell effect"**—for improving at skills you have not practiced

"Kettlebell Training...The Closest Thing You Can Get to Fighting, Without Throwing A Punch"

—Federal Counterterrorist Operator

The kettlebell. AK-47 of physical training hardware. Hunk of iron on a handle. Simple, sinister, brutal—and ferociously effective for developing explosive strength, dramatic power and never-say-die conditioning. The man's man's choice for the toughest, most demanding, highest-yield exercise tool on the planet. Guaranteed to forge a rugged, resilient, densely-muscled frame—built to withstand the hardest beating and dish it right back out, 24/7.

Once the prized and jealously-guarded training secret of elite Russian athletes, old-school strongmen and the military, the kettlebell has invaded the West. And taken no prisoners—thanks to former **Soviet Special Forces** physical training instructor and strength author, *Pavel Tsatsouline's* 2001 publication of *The Russian Kettlebell Challenge* and his manufacture of the first traditional Russian kettlebell in modern America.

American hardmen of all stripes were quick to recognize what their Russian counterparts had long known—nothing, nothing beats the kettlebell, when you're looking for a single tool to dramatically impact your strength and conditioning. A storm of success has swept the American S & C landscape, as kettlebell "Comrades" have busted through to new PRs, broken records, thrashed their opponents and elevated their game to new heights of excellence.

With *Enter the Kettlebell!* Pavel delivers a significant upgrade to his original landmark work, *The Russian Kettlebell Challenge.* Drawing on five years of developing and leading the world's first and premiere kettlebell instructor certification program, and after spending five years of additional research into what really works for dramatic results with the kettlebell—we have *Enter the Kettlebell!*

Pavel lays out a foolproof master system that guarantees you success—if you simply follow the commands!

- **Develop** all-purpose strength—to easily handle the toughest and most unexpected demand
- **Maximize** staying power—because the last round decides all
- **Forge** a fighter's physique—because the form must follow the function

Enter the kettlebell! and follow the plan:

1. The New RKC Program Minimum

With just two kettlebell exercises, takes you from raw newbie to solid contender—well-conditioned, flexible, resilient and muscular in all the right places.

2. The RKC Rite of Passage

Jumps you to the next level of physical excellence with Pavel's proven RKC formula for exceptional strength and conditioning.

3. Become a Man Among Men

Propels you to a Special Forces level of conditioning and earns you the right to call yourself a man.

When you rise to the challenge—and *Enter the Kettlebell!*—there will be no more confusion, no more uncertainty and no more excuses—only raw power, never-quit conditioning and earned respect.

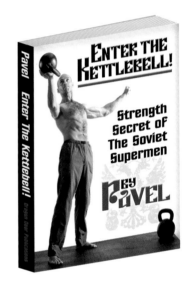

Stay informed of the latest advances in strength and conditioning by visiting:
WWW.RUSSIANKETTLEBELLS.COM

Visit www.russiankettlebells.com and sign up for Pavel Tsatsouline's free monthly e-newsletter, giving you late-breaking news and tips on how to stay ahead of the fitness pack.

Visit www.kbforum.dragondoor.com and participate in Dragon Door's stimulating and informative **Strength and Conditioning** Forum. Post your fitness questions or comments and get quick feedback from Pavel Tsatsouline and other leading fitness experts.

Visit www.dragondoor.com and browse the **Articles** section and other pages for ground-breaking theories and products for improving your health and well being.

DRAGON DOOR PUBLICATIONS PRESENTS
HARD-STYLE
HARD CORE TOOLS FOR HARD LIVING TYPES

1·800·899·5111
24 HOURS A DAY
FAX YOUR ORDER (866) 280-7619

ORDERING INFORMATION

Customer Service Questions? Please call us between 9:00am– 11:00pm EST Monday to Friday at 1-800-899-5111. Local and foreign customers call 513-346-4160 for orders and customer service

100% One-Year Risk-Free Guarantee. If you are not completely satisfied with any product—we'll be happy to give you a prompt exchange, credit, or refund, as you wish. Simply return your purchase to us,

and please let us know why you were dissatisfied—it will help us to provide better products and services in the future. *Shipping and handling fees are non-refundable.*

Telephone Orders For faster service you may place your orders by calling Toll Free 24 hours a day, 7 days a week, 365 days per year. When you call, please have your credit card ready.

Complete and mail with full payment to: Dragon Door Publications, 5 East County Rd B, #3, Little Canada, MN 55117

Please print clearly

Sold To: A

Name_____

Street _____

City _____

State _____ Zip _____

Day phone*_____
* Important for clarifying questions on orders

Please print clearly

SHIP TO: *(Street address for delivery)* B

Name_____

Street _____

City _____

State _____ Zip _____

Email _____

Warning to foreign customers:
The Customs in your country may or may not tax or otherwise charge you an additional fee for goods you receive. Dragon Door Publications is charging you only for U.S. handling and international shipping. Dragon Door Publications is in no way responsible for any additional fees levied by Customs, the carrier or any other entity.

ITEM #	QTY.	ITEM DESCRIPTION	ITEM PRICE	A OR B	TOTAL

Do You Have A Friend Who'd Like To Receive This Catalog?

We would be happy to send your friend a free copy. Make sure to print and complete in full:

Name ....

Address ....

City .... State .... Zip ......

HANDLING AND SHIPPING CHARGES • NO COD'S
Total Amount of Order Add (Excludes kettlebells and kettlebell kits):

$00.00 to 29.99	Add $6.00	$100.00 to 129.99	Add $14.00
$30.00 to 49.99	Add $7.00	$130.00 to 169.99	Add $16.00
$50.00 to 69.99	Add $8.00	$170.00 to 199.99	Add $18.00
$70.00 to 99.99	Add $11.00	$200.00 to 299.99	Add $20.00
		$300.00 and up	Add $24.00

Canada and Mexico add $6.00 to US charges. All other countries, flat rate, double US Charges. See Kettlebell section for Kettlebell Shipping and handling charges.

Total of Goods	
Shipping Charges	
Rush Charges	
Kettlebell Shipping Charges	
OH residents add 6.25% sales tax	
MN residents add 7.125% sales tax	
TOTAL ENCLOSED	

Do You Have A Friend Who'd Like To Receive This Catalog?

We would be happy to send your friend a free copy. Make sure to print and complete in full:

Name ....

Address ....

City .... State .... Zip ......

METHOD OF PAYMENT ❐ CHECK ❐ M.O. ❐ MASTERCARD ❐ VISA ❐ DISCOVER ❐ AMEX

Account No. *(Please indicate all the numbers on your credit card)*   EXPIRATION DATE

☐☐☐☐ ☐☐☐☐ ☐☐☐☐ ☐☐☐☐   ☐☐/☐☐

Day Phone: (   )_____

Signature: _____   **Date:** _____

NOTE: *We ship best method available for your delivery address. Foreign orders are sent by air. Credit card or International M.O. only. For* **RUSH** *processing of your order, add an additional $10.00 per address. Available on money order & charge card orders only.*

Errors and omissions excepted. Prices subject to change without notice.

ORDERING INFORMATION

Customer Service Questions? Please call us between 9:00am– 11:00pm EST Monday to Friday at 1-800-899-5111. Local and foreign customers call 513-346-4160 for orders and customer service

100% One-Year Risk-Free Guarantee. If you are not completely satisfied with any product—we'll be happy to give you a prompt exchange, credit, or refund, as you wish. Simply return your purchase to us, and please let us know why you were dissatisfied—it will help us to provide better products and services in the future. *Shipping and handling fees are non-refundable.*

Telephone Orders For faster service you may place your orders by calling Toll Free 24 hours a day, 7 days a week, 365 days per year. When you call, please have your credit card ready.

1·800·899·5111
24 HOURS A DAY
FAX YOUR ORDER (866) 280-7619

Complete and mail with full payment to: Dragon Door Publications, 5 East County Rd B, #3, Little Canada, MN 55117

Please print clearly

Sold To: **A**

Name_____

Street_____

City_____

State_____ Zip_____

Day phone*_____
* Important for clarifying questions on orders

Please print clearly

SHIP TO: *(Street address for delivery)*   **B**

Name_____

Street_____

City_____

State_____ Zip_____

Email_____

Item #	Qty.	Item Description	Item Price	A or B	Total

HANDLING AND SHIPPING CHARGES · NO COD'S
Total Amount of Order Add (Excludes kettlebells and kettlebell kits):

$00.00 to 29.99	Add $6.00	$100.00 to 129.99	Add $14.00
$30.00 to 49.99	Add $7.00	$130.00 to 169.99	Add $16.00
$50.00 to 69.99	Add $8.00	$170.00 to 199.99	Add $18.00
$70.00 to 99.99	Add $11.00	$200.00 to 299.99	Add $20.00
		$300.00 and up	Add $24.00

Canada and Mexico add $6.00 to US charges. All other countries, flat rate, double US Charges. See Kettlebell section for Kettlebell Shipping and handling charges.

Total of Goods	
Shipping Charges	
Rush Charges	
Kettlebell Shipping Charges	
OH residents add 6.25% sales tax	
MN residents add 7.125% sales tax	
Total Enclosed	

METHOD OF PAYMENT ❑ Check ❑ M.O. ❑ Mastercard ❑ Visa ❑ Discover ❑ Amex

Account No. *(Please indicate all the numbers on your credit card)*   EXPIRATION DATE

▢▢▢▢ ▢▢▢▢ ▢▢▢▢ ▢▢▢▢   ▢▢/▢▢

Day Phone: (   )_____

Signature: _____ **Date:** _____

NOTE: *We ship best method available for your delivery address. Foreign orders are sent by air. Credit card or International M.O. only. For RUSH processing of your order, add an additional $10.00 per address. Available on money order & charge card orders only.*

Errors and omissions excepted. Prices subject to change without notice.

Do You Have A Friend Who'd Like To Receive This Catalog?

We would be happy to send your friend a free copy. Make sure to print and complete in full:

Name

Address

City   State   Zip

Do You Have A Friend Who'd Like To Receive This Catalog?

We would be happy to send your friend a free copy. Make sure to print and complete in full:

Name

Address

City   State   Zip

ORDERING INFORMATION

1·800·899·5111
24 HOURS A DAY
FAX YOUR ORDER (866) 280-7619

Customer Service Questions? Please call us between 9:00am– 11:00pm EST Monday to Friday at 1-800-899-5111. Local and foreign customers call 513-346-4160 for orders and customer service

100% One-Year Risk-Free Guarantee. If you are not completely satisfied with any product—we'll be happy to give you a prompt exchange, credit, or refund, as you wish. Simply return your purchase to us,

and please let us know why you were dissatisfied—it will help us to provide better products and services in the future. *Shipping and handling fees are non-refundable.*

Telephone Orders For faster service you may place your orders by calling Toll Free 24 hours a day, 7 days a week, 365 days per year. When you call, please have your credit card ready.

Complete and mail with full payment to: Dragon Door Publications, 5 East County Rd B, #3, Little Canada, MN 55117

Please print clearly

Sold To: A

Name_____

Street _____

City _____

State _____ Zip _____

Day phone*_____
* Important for clarifying questions on orders

Please print clearly

SHIP TO: *(Street address for delivery)*   B

Name_____

Street _____

City _____

State _____ Zip _____

Email _____

Warning to foreign customers: The Customs in your country may or may not tax or otherwise charge you an additional fee for goods you receive. Dragon Door Publications is charging you only for U.S. handling and international shipping. Dragon Door Publications is in no way responsible for any additional fees levied by Customs, the carrier or any other entity.

ITEM #	QTY.	ITEM DESCRIPTION	ITEM PRICE	A OR B	TOTAL

Do You Have A Friend Who'd Like To Receive This Catalog?

We would be happy to send your friend a free copy. Make sure to print and complete in full:

Name _____

Address _____

City _____ State _____ Zip _____

HANDLING AND SHIPPING CHARGES • NO COD'S
Total Amount of Order Add (Excludes kettlebells and kettlebell kits):

$00.00 to 29.99	Add $6.00	$100.00 to 129.99	Add $14.00
$30.00 to 49.99	Add $7.00	$130.00 to 169.99	Add $16.00
$50.00 to 69.99	Add $8.00	$170.00 to 199.99	Add $18.00
$70.00 to 99.99	Add $11.00	$200.00 to 299.99	Add $20.00
		$300.00 and up	Add $24.00

Canada and Mexico add $6.00 to US charges. All other countries, flat rate, double US Charges. See Kettlebell section for Kettlebell Shipping and handling charges.

Total of Goods	
Shipping Charges	
Rush Charges	
Kettlebell Shipping Charges	
OH residents add 6.25% sales tax	
MN residents add 7.125% sales tax	
TOTAL ENCLOSED	

Do You Have A Friend Who'd Like To Receive This Catalog?

We would be happy to send your friend a free copy. Make sure to print and complete in full:

Name _____

Address _____

City _____ State _____ Zip _____

METHOD OF PAYMENT ❏ CHECK ❏ M.O. ❏ MASTERCARD ❏ VISA ❏ DISCOVER ❏ AMEX

Account No. *(Please indicate all the numbers on your credit card)*   EXPIRATION DATE

☐☐☐☐ ☐☐☐☐ ☐☐☐☐ ☐☐☐☐   ☐☐/☐☐

Day Phone: (   )_____

Signature: _____   **Date:** _____

NOTE: *We ship best method available for your delivery address. Foreign orders are sent by air. Credit card or International M.O. only. For* **RUSH** *processing of your order, add an additional $10.00 per address. Available on money order & charge card orders only.*

Errors and omissions excepted. Prices subject to change without notice.

DRAGON DOOR PUBLICATIONS PRESENTS

HARD-STYLE
HARD CORE TOOLS FOR HARD LIVING TYPES

1·800·899·5111
24 HOURS A DAY
FAX YOUR ORDER (866) 280-7619

ORDERING INFORMATION

Customer Service Questions? Please call us between 9:00am– 11:00pm EST Monday to Friday at 1-800-899-5111. Local and foreign customers call 513-346-4160 for orders and customer service

100% One-Year Risk-Free Guarantee. If you are not completely satisfied with any product—we'll be happy to give you a prompt exchange, credit, or refund, as you wish. Simply return your purchase to us,

and please let us know why you were dissatisfied—it will help us to provide better products and services in the future. *Shipping and handling fees are non-refundable.*

Telephone Orders For faster service you may place your orders by calling Toll Free 24 hours a day, 7 days a week, 365 days per year. When you call, please have your credit card ready.

Complete and mail with full payment to: Dragon Door Publications, 5 East County Rd B, #3, Little Canada, MN 55117

Please print clearly

Sold To: A

Name_____

Street _____

City _____

State _____ Zip _____

Day phone*_____
* Important for clarifying questions on orders

Please print clearly

SHIP TO: *(Street address for delivery)*   B

Name_____

Street _____

City _____

State _____ Zip _____

Email _____

Warning to foreign customers:
The Customs in your country may or may not tax or otherwise charge you an additional fee for goods you receive. Dragon Door Publications is charging you only for U.S. handling and international shipping. Dragon Door Publications is in no way responsible for any additional fees levied by Customs, the carrier or any other entity.

ITEM #	QTY.	ITEM DESCRIPTION	ITEM PRICE	A OR B	TOTAL

Do You Have A Friend Who'd Like To Receive This Catalog?

We would be happy to send your friend a free copy. Make sure to print and complete in full:

Name _____

Address _____

City _____ State ____ Zip ____

HANDLING AND SHIPPING CHARGES • NO COD'S
Total Amount of Order Add (Excludes kettlebells and kettlebell kits):

$00.00 to 29.99	Add $6.00	$100.00 to 129.99	Add $14.00
$30.00 to 49.99	Add $7.00	$130.00 to 169.99	Add $16.00
$50.00 to 69.99	Add $8.00	$170.00 to 199.99	Add $18.00
$70.00 to 99.99	Add $11.00	$200.00 to 299.99	Add $20.00
		$300.00 and up	Add $24.00

Canada and Mexico add $6.00 to US charges. All other countries, flat rate, double US Charges. See Kettlebell section for Kettlebell Shipping and handling charges.

Total of Goods	
Shipping Charges	
Rush Charges	
Kettlebell Shipping Charges	
OH residents add 6.25% sales tax	
MN residents add 7.125% sales tax	
TOTAL ENCLOSED	

Do You Have A Friend Who'd Like To Receive This Catalog?

We would be happy to send your friend a free copy. Make sure to print and complete in full:

Name _____

Address _____

City _____ State ____ Zip ____

METHOD OF PAYMENT ❑ CHECK ❑ M.O. ❑ MASTERCARD ❑ VISA ❑ DISCOVER ❑ AMEX

Account No. *(Please indicate all the numbers on your credit card)*   EXPIRATION DATE

☐☐☐☐ ☐☐☐☐ ☐☐☐☐ ☐☐☐☐   ☐☐/☐☐

Day Phone: (   )_____

Signature: _____   **Date:** _____

NOTE: *We ship best method available for your delivery address. Foreign orders are sent by air. Credit card or International M.O. only. For* **RUSH** *processing of your order, add an additional $10.00 per address. Available on money order & charge card orders only.*

Errors and omissions excepted. Prices subject to change without notice.

ORDERING INFORMATION

1·800·899·5111
24 HOURS A DAY
FAX YOUR ORDER (866) 280-7619

Customer Service Questions? Please call us between 9:00am– 11:00pm EST Monday to Friday at 1-800-899-5111. Local and foreign customers call 513-346-4160 for orders and customer service

100% One-Year Risk-Free Guarantee. If you are not completely satisfied with any product—we'll be happy to give you a prompt exchange, credit, or refund, as you wish. Simply return your purchase to us, and please let us know why you were dissatisfied—it will help us to provide better products and services in the future. *Shipping and handling fees are non-refundable.*

Telephone Orders For faster service you may place your orders by calling Toll Free 24 hours a day, 7 days a week, 365 days per year. When you call, please have your credit card ready.

Complete and mail with full payment to: Dragon Door Publications, 5 East County Rd B, #3, Little Canada, MN 55117

Please print clearly

Sold To: A

Name_____

Street_____

City_____

State_____ Zip_____

Day phone*_____
* Important for clarifying questions on orders

Please print clearly

SHIP TO: *(Street address for delivery)*   B

Name_____

Street_____

City_____

State_____ Zip_____

Email_____

Warning to foreign customers: The Customs in your country may or may not tax or otherwise charge you an additional fee for goods you receive. Dragon Door Publications is charging you only for U.S. handling and international shipping. Dragon Door Publications is in no way responsible for any additional fees levied by Customs, the carrier or any other entity.

ITEM #	QTY.	ITEM DESCRIPTION	ITEM PRICE	A OR B	TOTAL

Do You Have A Friend Who'd Like To Receive This Catalog?

We would be happy to send your friend a free copy. Make sure to print and complete in full:

Name

Address

City   State   Zip

HANDLING AND SHIPPING CHARGES · NO COD'S
Total Amount of Order Add (Excludes kettlebells and kettlebell kits):

$00.00 to 29.99	Add $6.00	$100.00 to 129.99	Add $14.00
$30.00 to 49.99	Add $7.00	$130.00 to 169.99	Add $16.00
$50.00 to 69.99	Add $8.00	$170.00 to 199.99	Add $18.00
$70.00 to 99.99	Add $11.00	$200.00 to 299.99	Add $20.00
		$300.00 and up	Add $24.00

Canada and Mexico add $6.00 to US charges. All other countries, flat rate, double US Charges. See Kettlebell section for Kettlebell Shipping and handling charges.

Total of Goods	
Shipping Charges	
Rush Charges	
Kettlebell Shipping Charges	
OH residents add 6.25% sales tax	
MN residents add 7.125% sales tax	
TOTAL ENCLOSED	

Do You Have A Friend Who'd Like To Receive This Catalog?

We would be happy to send your friend a free copy. Make sure to print and complete in full:

Name

Address

City   State   Zip

METHOD OF PAYMENT ❑ CHECK ❑ M.O. ❑ MASTERCARD ❑ VISA ❑ DISCOVER ❑ AMEX

Account No. *(Please indicate all the numbers on your credit card)*   EXPIRATION DATE

☐☐☐☐ ☐☐☐☐ ☐☐☐☐ ☐☐☐☐   ☐☐/☐☐

Day Phone: (   )_____

Signature: _____ **Date:** _____

NOTE: *We ship best method available for your delivery address. Foreign orders are sent by air. Credit card or International M.O. only. For* **RUSH** *processing of your order, add an additional $10.00 per address. Available on money order & charge card orders only.*

Errors and omissions excepted. Prices subject to change without notice.